11+
Non-verbal Reasoning

WORKBOOK 4

Additional Practice Questions

Dr Stephen C Curran
with Andrea Richardson
Edited by Katrina MacKay

This book belongs to

Shreya D

ae
PUBLICATIONS

Accelerated Education Publications Ltd

Contents

Chapter Seventeen
ODD ONE OUT
1. Basic Level

Exercise 17: 1 Which figure does not fit in with the others?

1)

  a   b   c   d   e

2)

  a   b   c   d   e

3)

  a   b   c   d   e

4)

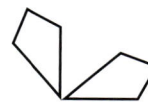

  a   b   c   d   e

5)

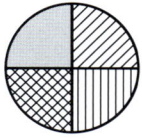

a   **(b)**   c   d   e

6)

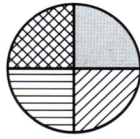

a   b   **(c)**   d   e

7)

(a)   b   c   d   e

8)

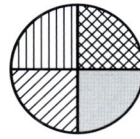

a   **(b)**   c   d   e

9)

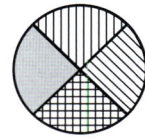

(a)   b   c   d   e

10)

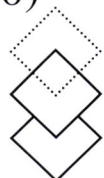

a   b   **(c)**   d   e

11)

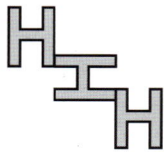

a   b   c   d   (e)

12)

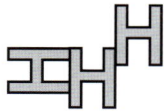

a   b   c   (d)   e

13)

a   b   (c)   d   (e)

14)

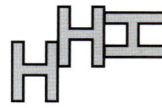

(a)   b   c   d   e

15)

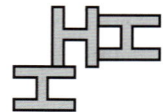

(a)   b   c   d   e

16)

a   b   (c)   d   e

17)

a   (b)   c   d   e

18)

a   b   c   d   (e)

19)

a   b   (c)   d   e

20)

a   (b)   c   d   e

Score

2. Intermediate Level

In each of the rows below there are five figures. Find one figure in each row that is **most unlike** the other four.

Example

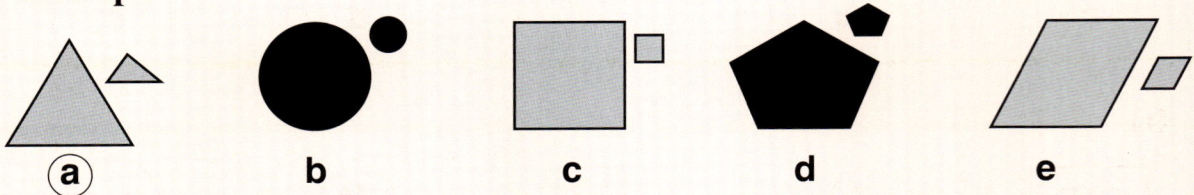

a   b   c   d   e

Answer: **a** as the smaller shape is not the same as the larger shape.

Exercise 17: 2 Which figure does not fit in with the others?

1)

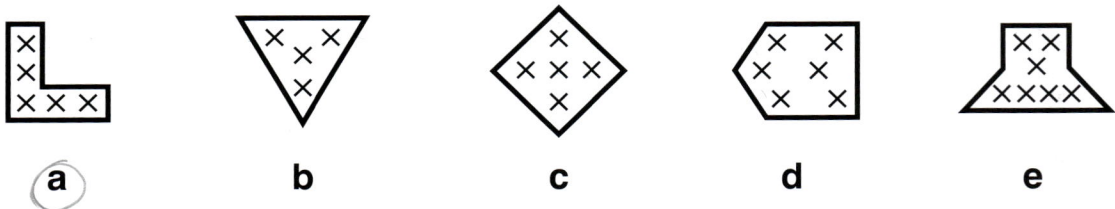

a   b   c   d   e

2)

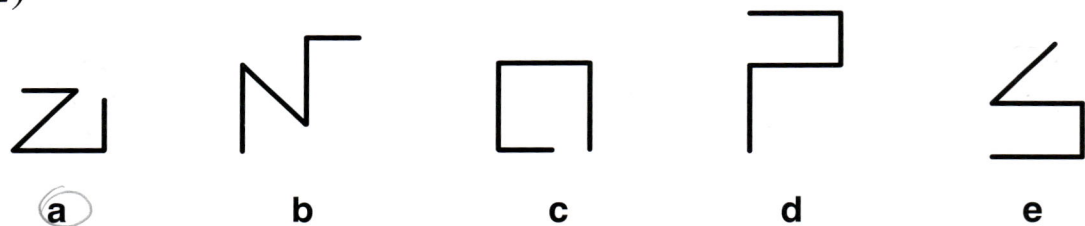

a   b   c   d   e

3)

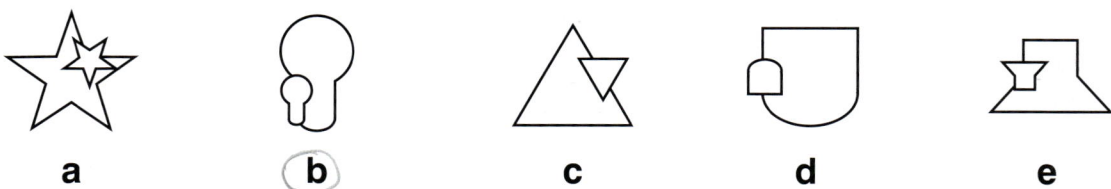

a   b   c   d   e

4)

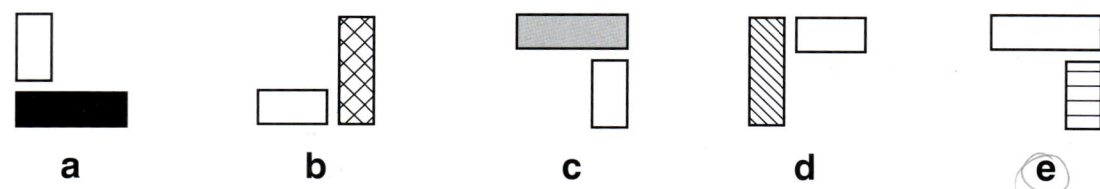

a   b   c   d   e

5)

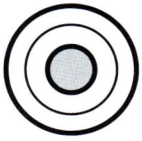         

a   (b)   c   d   e

6)

a   b   c   d   (e)

7)

a   (b)   c   d   e

8)

a   b   c   (d)   e

9)

a   b   c   d   (e)

10)

   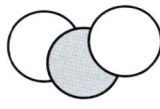   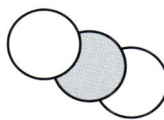      

a   (b)   c   d   e

11)

    a   b   c   d   (e)

12)

    a   (b)   c   d   e

13)

    a   b   c   d   (e)

14)

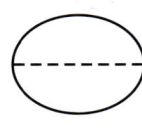

    a   b   c   d   (e)

15)

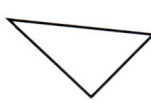

    a   (b)   c   d   e

16)

a   b   c   d   e

17)

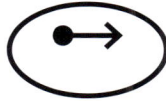 

a   b   c   d   e

18)

 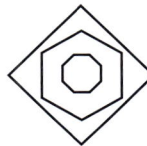 

a   b   c   d   e

19)

  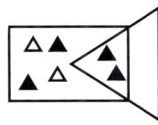  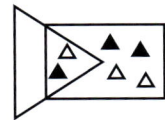

a   b   c   d   e

20)

a   b   c   d   e

Score

3. Advanced Level

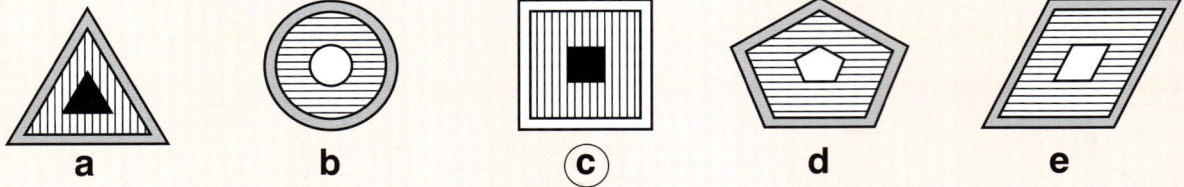

Exercise 17: 3 Which figure does not fit in with the others?

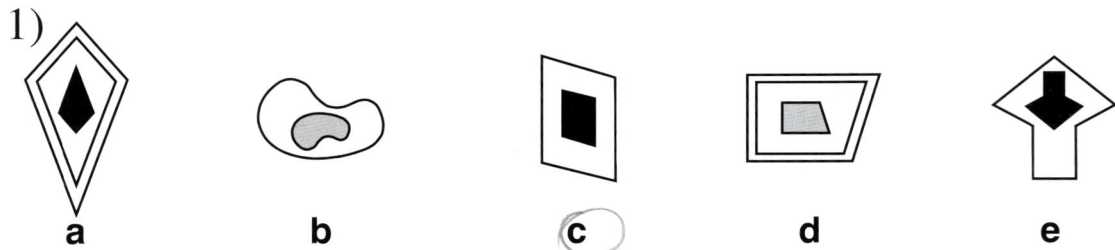

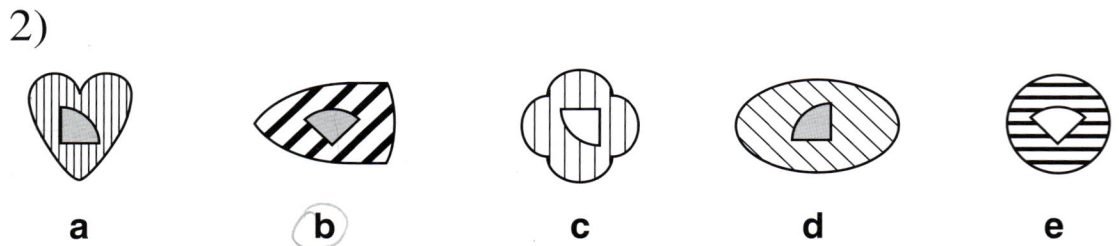

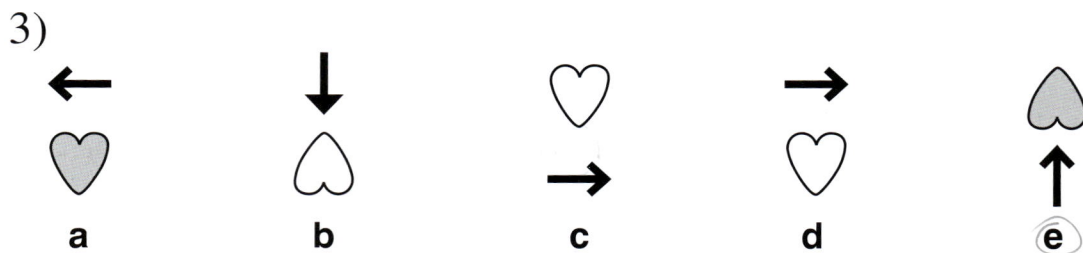

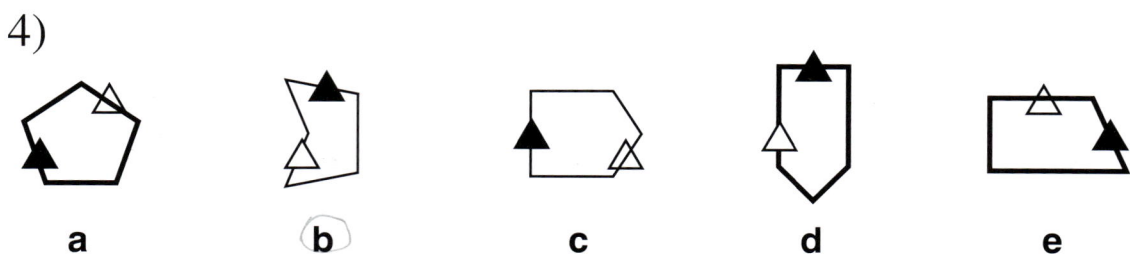

1) a   b   c   d   e

2) a   b   c   d   e

3) a   b   c   d   e

4) a   b   c   d   e

5)

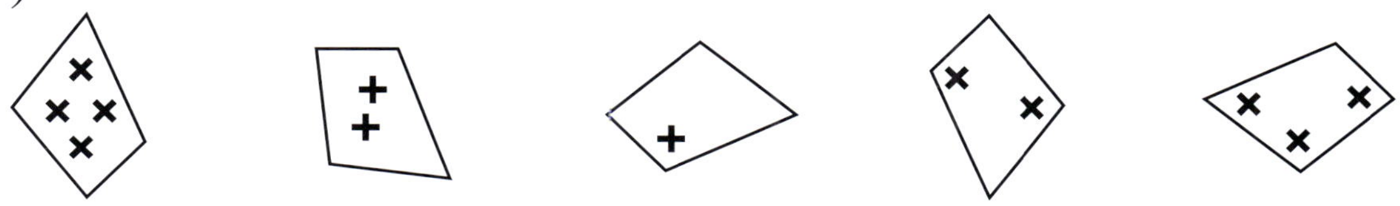

a   b   c   d   e

6)

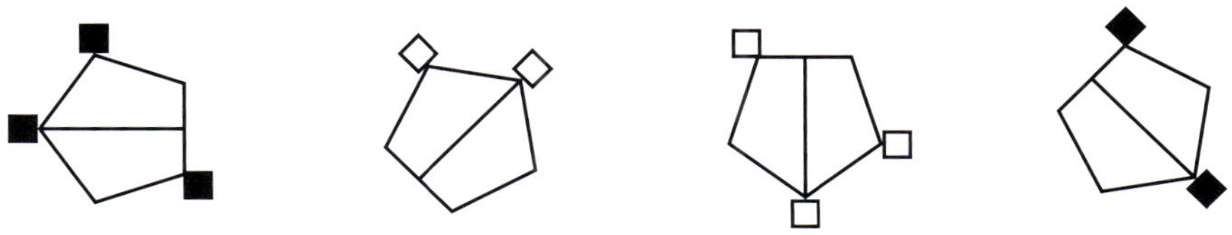

a   b   c   d   e

7)

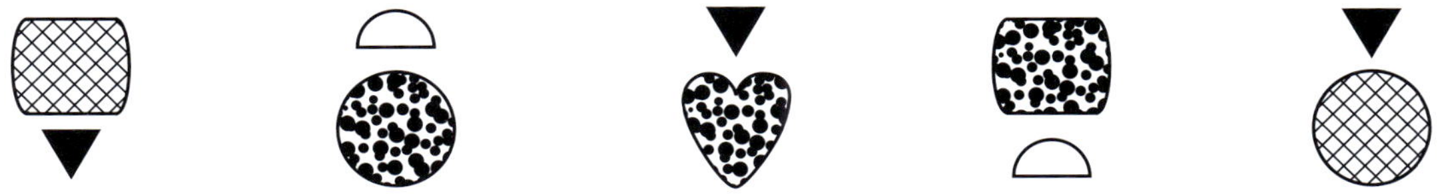

a   b   c   d   e

8)

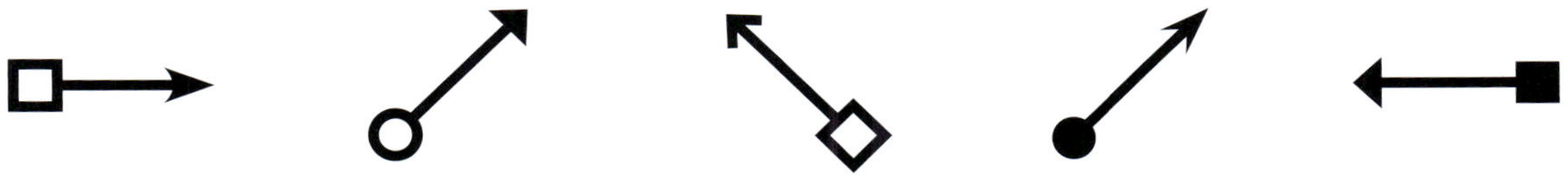

a   b   c   d   e

9)

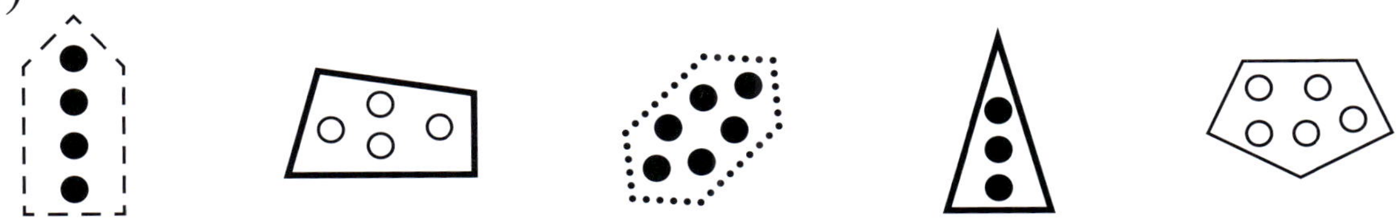

a   b   c   d   e

10)

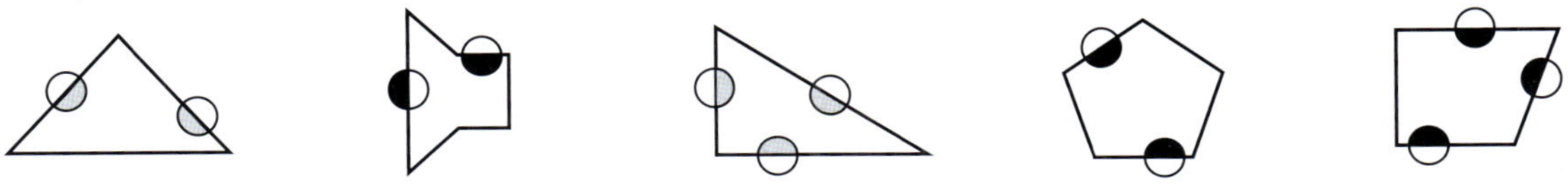

a   b   c   d   e

11)

   a   b   c   d   e

12)

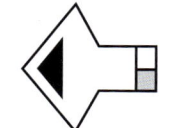 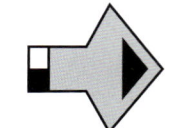 

   a   b   c   d   e

13)

   a   b   c   d   e

14)

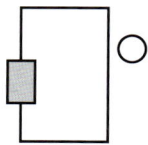 

   a   b   c   d   e

15)

   a   b   c   d   e

14

16)

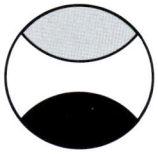

a   b   c   d   e

17)

a   b   c   d   e

18)

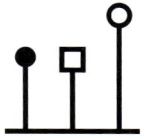 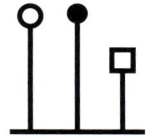 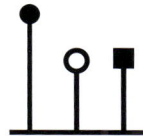 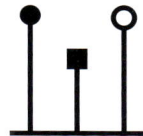 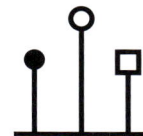

a   b   c   d   e

19)

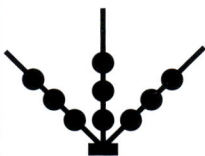  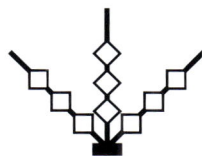

a   b   c   d   e

20)

a   b   c   d   e

Score

4. Higher Level

In each of the rows below there are five figures. Find one figure in each row that is **most unlike** the other four.

Example

      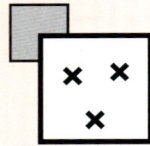      

   a   ⓑ   **c**   **d**   **e**

Answer: **b** as there should be one less Cross than the number of sides in the shape.

Exercise 17: 4   Which figure does not fit in with the others?

1)

   ⓐ   **b**   **c**   **d**   **e**

2)

   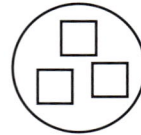

   a   **b**   **c**   **d**   **e**

3)

   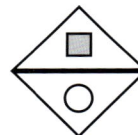   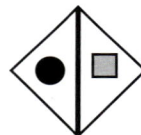

   a   **b**   **c**   **d**   **e**

4)

   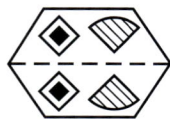      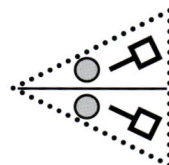 

   a   **b**   **c**   **d**   **e**

5)

a   b   c   d   e

6)

a   b   c   d   e

7)

a   b   c   d   e

8)

a   b   c   d   e

9)

a   b   c   d   e

10)

            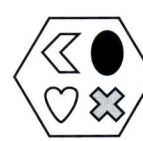

a   b   c   d   e

11)

  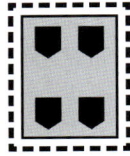  

   a   **b**   **c**   **d**   **e**

12)

   a   **b**   **c**   **d**    **e**

13)

   a   **b**   **c**   **d**   **e**

14)

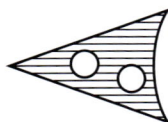 

   a   **b**   **c**   **d**   **e**

15)

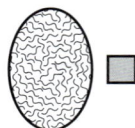 

   a   **b**   **c**   **d**   **e**

16)

a   **b**   **c**   **d**   **e**

17)

a   **b**   **c**   **d**   **e**

18)

a   **b**   **c**   **d**   **e**

19)

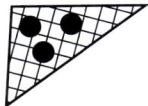 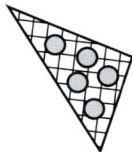 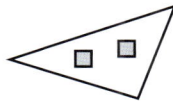  

a   **b**   **c**   **d**   **e**

20)

a   **b**   **c**   **d**   **e**

Score

5. Mixed Levels

Exercise 17: 5 Which figure does not fit in with the others?

1)

   a   **b**   **c**   **d**   **e**

2)

   a   **b**   **c**   **d**   **e**

3)

   a   **b**   **c**   **d**   **e**

4)

   a   **b**   **c**   **d**   **e**

5)

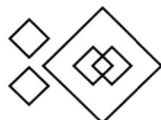

   a   **b**   **c**   **d**   **e**

6)

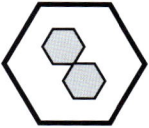

a   b   c   d   e

7)

a   b   c   d   e

8)

a   b   c   d   e

9)

a   b   c   d   e

10)

a   b   c   d   e

11)

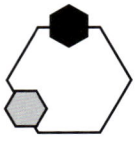   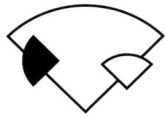   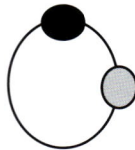   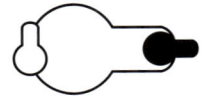

a   **b**   **c**   **d**   **e**

12)

a   **b**   **c**   **d**   **e**

13)

a   **b**   **c**   **d**   **e**

14)

a   **b**   **c**   **d**   **e**

15)

   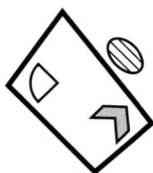         

a   **b**   **c**   **d**   **e**

16)

a   b   c   d   e

17)

a   b   c   d   e

18)

a   b   c   d   e

19)

a   b   c   d   e

20)

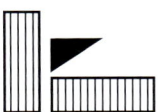 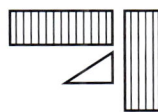 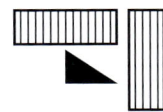

a   b   c   d   e

Score

Chapter Eighteen
CODES
1. Type 1 - Level Two

The following figures correspond to the codes below them. Decide how the code letters go with the figures and then find the correct code for the Test Figure.

Example   TEST FIGURE

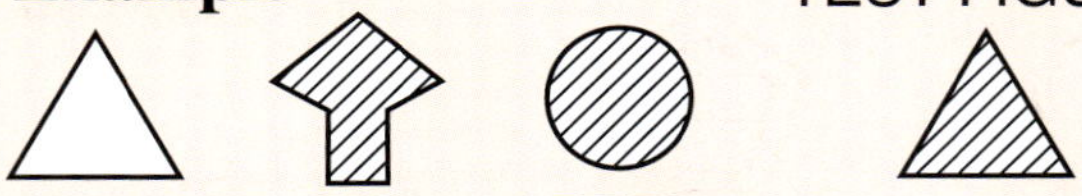

AR   BS   BT

BR   AS   AT   BS   AR
(a)   b   c   d   e

The **first letter** stands for the type of fill: **A** - White Fill; **B** - Shaded Fill.
The **second letter** stands for each shape: **R** - Triangle; **S** - Arrow; **T** - Circle.
The answer is **BR**: **B** for Shaded Fill; **R** for Triangle.

Exercise 18: 1 Find the code of the Test Figure.

1)   TEST FIGURE

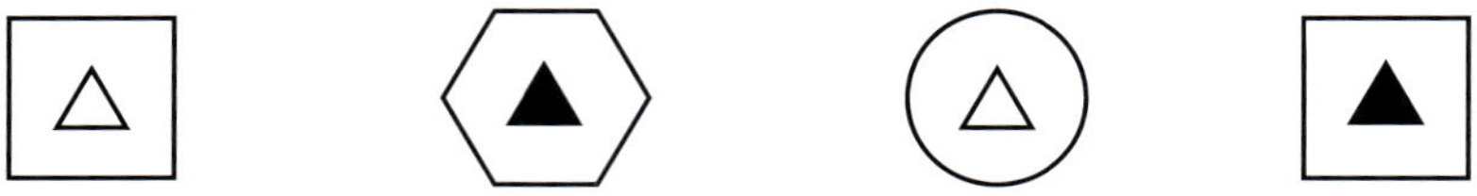

HP   JQ   KP

KQ   HP   KP
a   b   c

JP   HQ
d   (e)

2)   TEST FIGURE

SE   TF   SG

SF   TG   SG
a   (b)   c

TE   GT
d   e

3)   TEST FIGURE

AZ   BY   AX

BX   ZY   BZ
a   b   c

AY   AB
(d)   e

4)   TEST FIGURE

CM   DN   EM

DM   MN   EN
a   b   c

CM   CN
d   (e)

5)

CV   BW   AW   CX

TEST FIGURE

CW	AX	AV
a	**b**	**c**

BX	BV
d	**e**

6)

SJ   TK   UJ   SL

TEST FIGURE

SK	TJ	UK
a	**b**	**c**

TL	SL
d	**e**

7)

XO   YP   XP   ZQ

TEST FIGURE

YQ	YO	XQ
a	**b**	**c**

ZP	ZO
d	**e**

8)

EA   FA   EB   GC

TEST FIGURE

EC	FC	GA
a	**b**	**c**

FB	GB
d	**e**

9)

HM   JN   JM   KO

TEST FIGURE

JO	HN	KM
a	**b**	**c**

KN	HO
d	**e**

10)

AJ   BK   AL   CK

TEST FIGURE

AK	BL	CJ
a	**b**	**c**

CL	BJ
d	**e**

11)

LE	MF	LG	NE	OF

TEST FIGURE

NG	LF	NF
a	**b**	**c**

ME	MG
d	**e**

12)

JC	KD	JE	LD	KE

TEST FIGURE

LC	LE	KE
a	**b**	**c**

JD	KC
d	**e**

13)

ZA	YB	XC	WB	YD

TEST FIGURE

ZB	XD	WA
a	**b**	**c**

WC	YA
d	**e**

14)

PK	QL	RM	QN	RK

TEST FIGURE

RK	RL	PM
a	**b**	**c**

PN	QM
d	**e**

15)

AS	BT	BU	CS	AT

TEST FIGURE

AU	BS	CS
a	**b**	**c**

BA	CT
d	**e**

16)

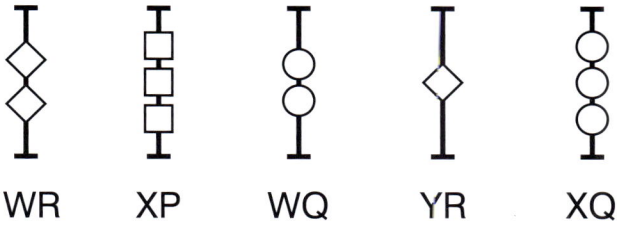

WR   XP   WQ   YR   XQ

TEST FIGURE

XR   WR   XQ
a   **b**   **c**

YP   YQ
d   **e**

---

17)

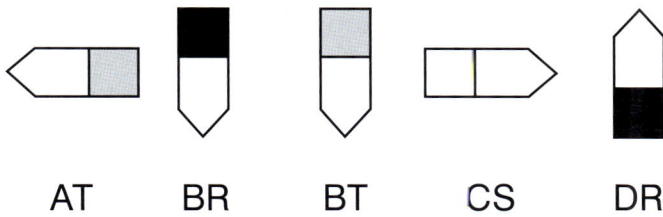

AT   BR   BT   CS   DR

TEST FIGURE

CT   DT   AS
a   **b**   **c**

AR   BS
d   **e**

---

18)

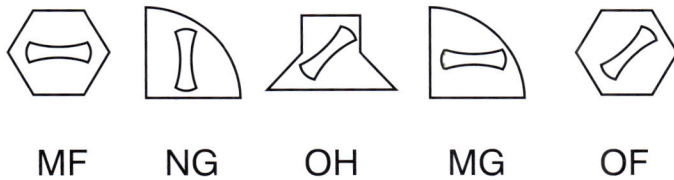

MF   NG   OH   MG   OF

TEST FIGURE

NH   MH   HF
a   **b**   **c**

NF   OG
d   **e**

---

19)

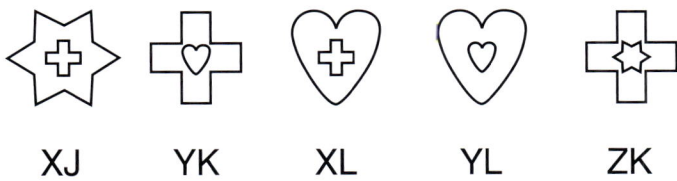

XJ   YK   XL   YL   ZK

TEST FIGURE

XK   YJ   ZL
a   **b**   **c**

XY   ZJ
d   **e**

---

20)

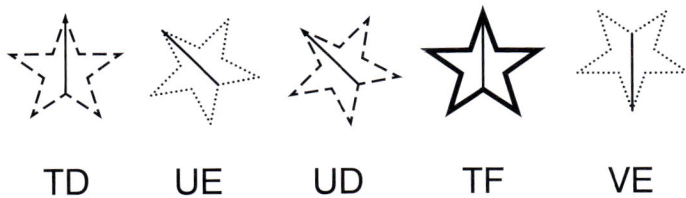

TD   UE   UD   TF   VE

TEST FIGURE

VD   UF   VF
a   **b**   **c**

TF   VE
d   **e**

Score

2. Type 2 - Level Two

The following figures correspond to the codes next to them. Decide how the code letters go with the figures and then find the correct code for the Test Figure.

Example

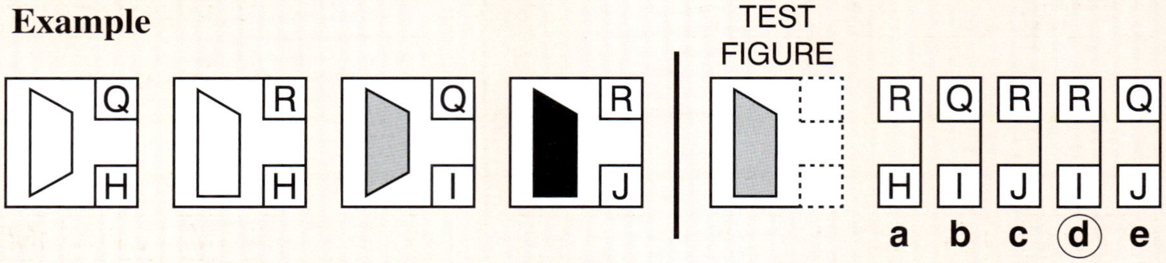

TEST FIGURE

The **top letter** stands for each shape: **Q** - Isosceles Trapezium Shape; **R** - Ordinary Trapezium Shape. The **bottom letter** stands for the type of fill: **H** - White Fill; **I** - Grey Fill; **J** - Black Fill. The answer is **RI**.

Exercise 18: 2 Find the code of the Test Figure.

1)

TEST FIGURE

L	N	M	N	M
Y	X	Z	Z	X

a **b** c d e

2)

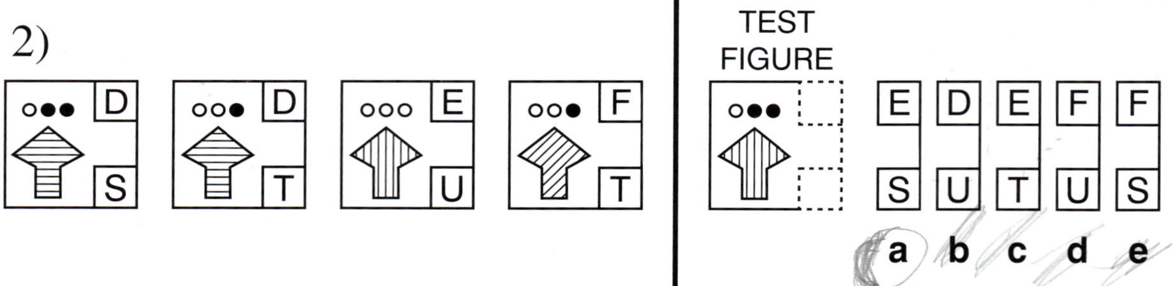

TEST FIGURE

E	D	E	F	F
S	U	T	U	S

a b c d e

3)

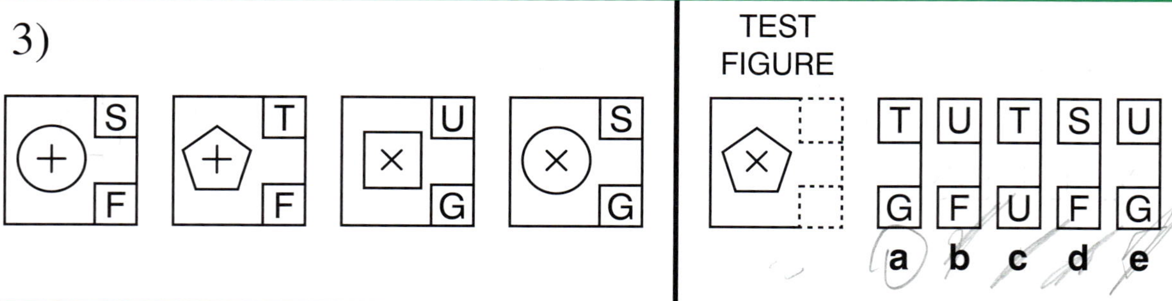

TEST FIGURE

T	U	T	S	U
G	F	U	F	G

a b c d e

4)

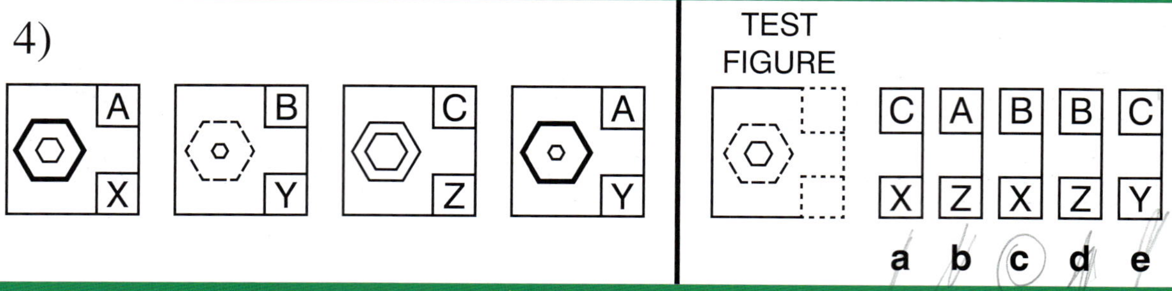

TEST FIGURE

C	A	B	B	C
X	Z	X	Z	Y

a b **c** d e

5)

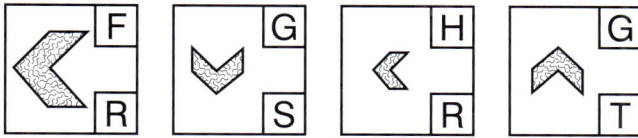

TEST FIGURE

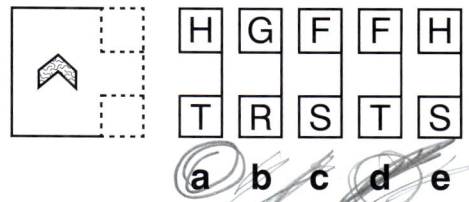

H	G	F	F	H
T	R	S	T	S

a b c d e

6)

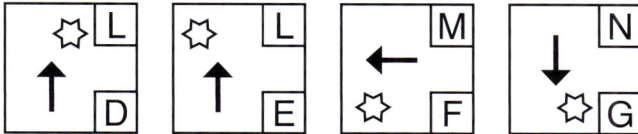

TEST FIGURE

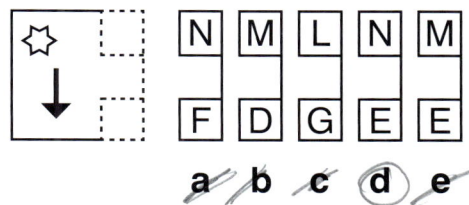

N	M	L	N	M
F	D	G	E	E

a b c **d** e

7)

TEST FIGURE

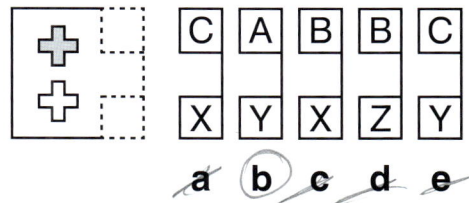

C	A	B	B	C
X	Y	X	Z	Y

a **b** c d e

8)

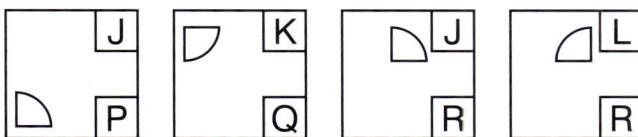

TEST FIGURE

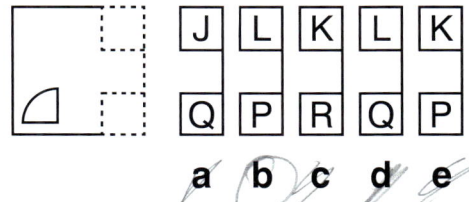

J	L	K	L	K
Q	P	R	Q	P

a b c d e

9)

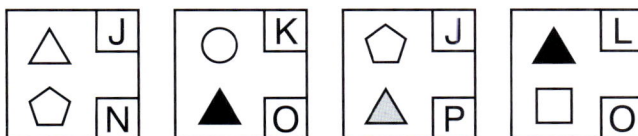

TEST FIGURE

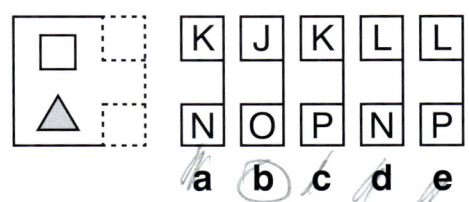

K	J	K	L	L
N	O	P	N	P

a **b** c d e

10)

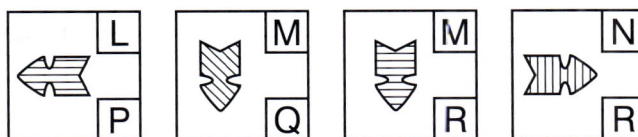

TEST FIGURE

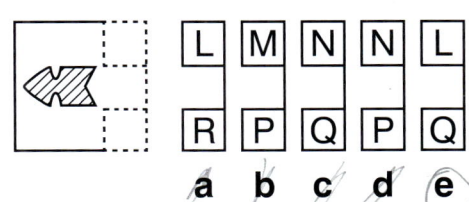

L	M	N	N	L
R	P	Q	P	Q

a b c d **e**

11)

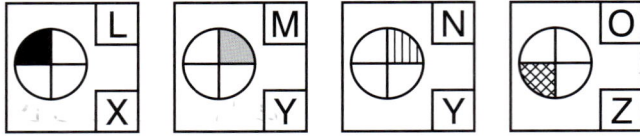

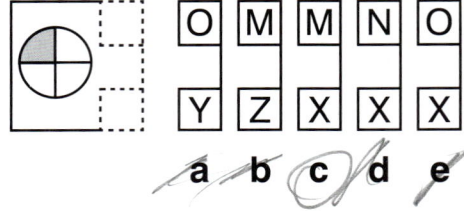

O	M	M	N	O
Y	Z	X	X	X

a b c d e

12)

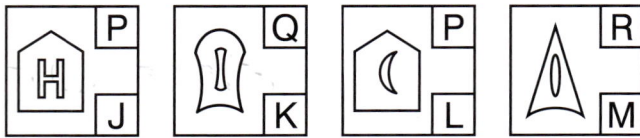

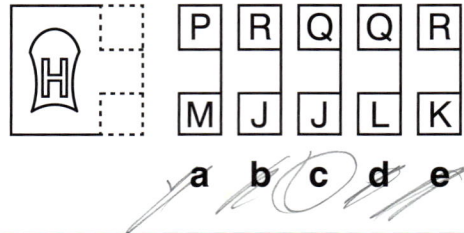

P	R	Q	Q	R
M	J	J	L	K

a b c d e

13)

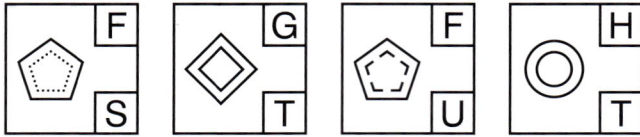

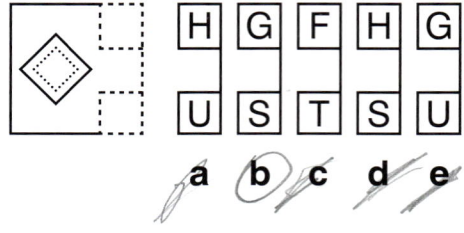

H	G	F	H	G
U	S	T	S	U

a b c d e

14)

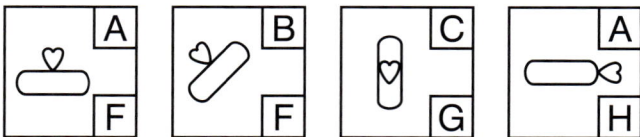

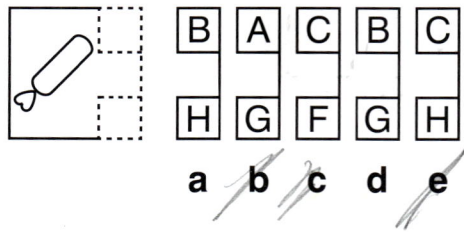

B	A	C	B	C
H	G	F	G	H

a b c d e

15)

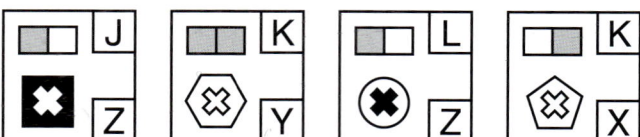

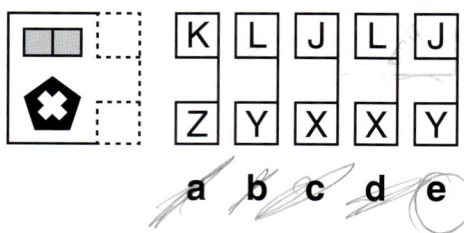

K	L	J	L	J
Z	Y	X	X	Y

a b c d e

16)

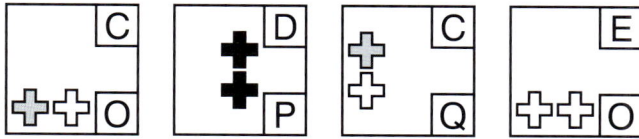

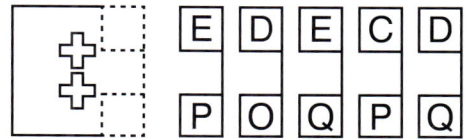

a b c d e

17)

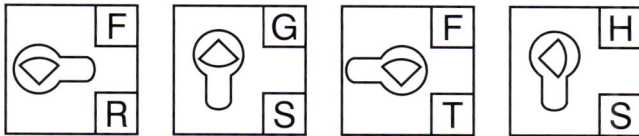

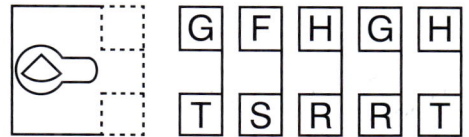

a b c d e

18)

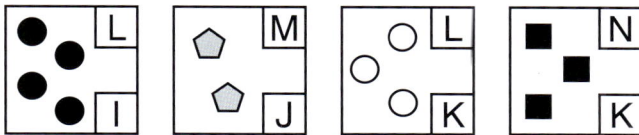

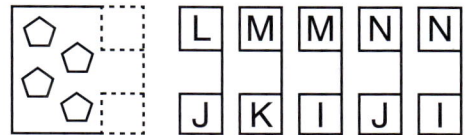

a b **c** d e

19)

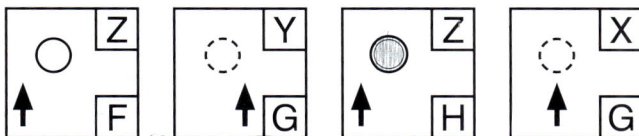

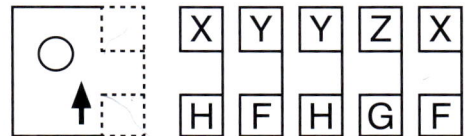

a **b** c d e

20)

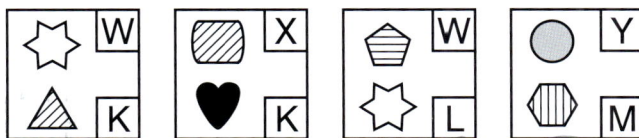

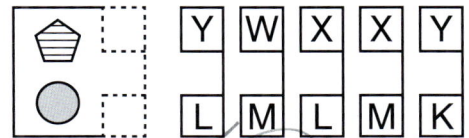

a b c d e

Score

3. Type 1 - Level Three

Exercise 18: 3 Find the code of the Test Figure.

1)

TEST FIGURE

| XCH | XEH | ZDG |
| **a** | **b** | **c** |

ZCG   XDG   ZEH

| XCG | XEG |
| **d** | **e** |

2)

TEST FIGURE

| RBV | PAV | PBU |
| **a** | **b** | **c** |

PAU   QBV   RAV

| PBV | QAU |
| **d** | **e** |

3)

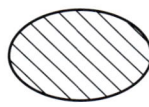 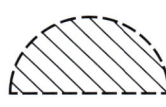

TEST FIGURE

| KAT | KBS | KBT |
| **a** | **b** | **c** |

KAS   LBS   MAT

| LBT | MBS |
| **d** | **e** |

4)

TEST FIGURE

| XFV | YEV | YGV |
| **a** | **b** | **c** |

XEV   YFW   XGW

| YEW | XFW |
| **d** | **e** |

5)

TEST FIGURE

QYK	PXL	QXJ
a	**b**	**c**

PYJ	QXL
d	**e**

PXJ   QYJ   QXK   PYL

6)

TEST FIGURE

HUN	HTN	ISN
a	**b**	**c**

HTM	GUM
d	**e**

GSM   GTN   HSN   IUM

7)

TEST FIGURE

CPB	DNA	CNB
a	**b**	**c**

DPA	DPB
d	**e**

CNA   DOB   COA   EPB

8)

TEST FIGURE

RMQ	SMQ	RMP
a	**b**	**c**

TLP	RLQ
d	**e**

RLP   SLQ   TMP   SNQ

9)

TEST FIGURE

AZL	CYL	AYK
a	**b**	**c**

BZK	AYL
d	**e**

AZK   BZL   BYK   CZK

10)

TEST FIGURE

ALZ	BMY	BLZ
a	**b**	**c**

ALY	AMZ
d	**e**

ALX   BLY   AMZ   BMX

11)

SPA   TQB   URA   VPB

TEST FIGURE

SPB	TQA	UPB
a	**b**	**c**
SQA	SQB	
d	**e**	

12)

TEA   TFB   UEC   UGA

TEST FIGURE

TFC	UGC	TGC
a	**b**	**c**
UFA	TGA	
d	**e**	

13)

RZC   RYD   RYE   QZF

TEST FIGURE

QYC	RZD	QYF
a	**b**	**c**
QZC	QYE	
d	**e**	

14)

ALE   BMF   CNG   COE

TEST FIGURE

BLE	ALF	COF
a	**b**	**c**
BLF	BMG	
d	**e**	

15)

JSB   KTA   LUB   JVA

TEST FIGURE

JVB	KVB	LTB
a	**b**	**c**
KVA	KSB	
d	**e**	

16)

TEST FIGURE

LCT	NDT	OCS
a	**b**	**c**

OBU	OCU
d	**e**

LAS   MBT   NCS   MDU   OAT

---

17)

TEST FIGURE

FXR	FYR	FYP
a	**b**	**c**

GYQ	FWR
d	**e**

EWP   FXQ   GXR   EYR   GWQ

---

18)

TEST FIGURE

ZIM	ZHM	YKM
a	**b**	**c**

XIN	ZIN
d	**e**

XHM   YIN   YJO   ZKN   XKO

---

19)

TEST FIGURE

ATM	AUO	BTM
a	**b**	**c**

ATO	CSM
d	**e**

ASM   BTN   BUO   CSN   DTM

---

20)

TEST FIGURE

RYT	RWS	QXS
a	**b**	**c**

RXT	RWT
d	**e**

PWR   QXR   QWS   RYS   QYT

Score

4. Type 1 - Level Four

Exercise 18: 4 Find the code of the Test Figure.

1)

TEST FIGURE

SXAK	SXBJ	SYAL
a	b	c

RZCL	SXBL	
d	e	

RXAJ   SYAK   SZBK   RYCL

2)

TEST FIGURE

REDW	PGCV	QGCV
a	b	c

PGDV	PFCW	
d	e	

PECW   QEDV   RFCV   QGDW

3)

TEST FIGURE

LDSG	MERH	MDTH
a	b	c

MEUG	MERF	
d	e	

LCRG   MDSH   LETG   MCUF

4)

TEST FIGURE

TXAM	SYCL	TXAL
a	b	c

SXCM	TYAL	
d	e	

RXAL   SYBM   RYBL   TXCM

5)

CXJP	BXKQ	AYLR	CZLS

TEST FIGURE

AXKR	BZKQ	AYJR
a	b	c

AYJQ	BYJQ
d	e

6)

META	NFTB	MGUB	NHUA

TEST FIGURE

NGTA	MEUB	NEUB
a	b	c

MEUA	MHTB
d	e

7)

KRZA	KSXB	MRZC	LTXA

TEST FIGURE

LSXC	KSXC	LSXA
a	b	c

LSZC	MRZB
d	e

8)

OGCR	OHDS	PHCT	QFCS

TEST FIGURE

PFDT	OFCR	PFDR
a	b	c

PHDR	QGDT
d	e

9)

DLZF	CMXF	BLZG	DNXG

TEST FIGURE

DMZF	DLXG	CNZG
a	b	c

DMZG	CMZF
d	e

10)

AZPJ	BYQK	CXRK	DYPL

TEST FIGURE

DXQJ	AYQL	DXQK
a	b	c

BXRJ	DZRK
d	e

11)

EZJA   FYKB   GXLA   FZMC

TEST FIGURE

EXMA	FXLB	EYLB
a	b	c

GZMB	EXMB
d	e

12)

RWFA   SWGB   TXFC   UYHA

TEST FIGURE

SYGB	RXGB	SXFA
a	b	c

RYFB	SXFB
d	e

13)

DJPX   CKPY   BJQY   AKQX

TEST FIGURE

DKPY	AKQY	DKQY
a	b	c

DJPY	BKQX
d	e

14)

SAJF   TBKF   UALG   TCLH

TEST FIGURE

SALG	SBKG	SBKF
a	b	c

TBKG	SCLF
d	e

15)

SAZK   SBYL   TBZM   UCXK

TEST FIGURE

SCXL	TAXL	TCZL
a	b	c

TBZK	TCZM
d	e

16)

TEST FIGURE

PMAF

QMBG

QNCF

ROCH

PNBF	PMAG	PNBG
a	**b**	**c**

QMCG	PNBH	
d	**e**	

17)

TEST FIGURE

DQZT

ERYU

FQXU

DSXV

FRZU	FRXU	DRZV
a	**b**	**c**

FSYV	FRZV	
d	**e**	

18)

TEST FIGURE

AJZN

BKYO

ALXP

CJXO

BLZP	BKZO	CLXP
a	**b**	**c**

BLYP	BLZN	
d	**e**	

19)

TEST FIGURE

XFMU

YGNV

ZFOV

XHNW

ZGMU	ZFOU	ZGOU
a	**b**	**c**

ZGOV	YGOW	
d	**e**	

20)

TEST FIGURE

QCXJ

QBYK

RAYL

SCZL

RAZJ	RBZJ	QAZL
a	**b**	**c**

RBZK	RAXJ	
d	**e**	

Score [ ]

5. Mixed Levels

Exercise 18: 5 Find the code of the Test Figure.

1)

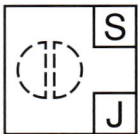

UP

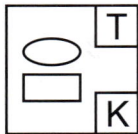

VQ

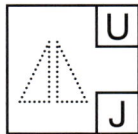

VR

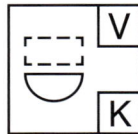

WS

TEST
FIGURE

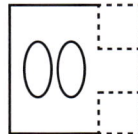

WQ	US	VP
a	**b**	**c**

UQ	UR
d	**e**

2)

S	T	U	V
J	K	J	K

TEST
FIGURE

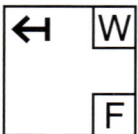

U	V	T	S	T
K	J	J	K	K
a	**b**	**c**	**d**	**e**

3)

LAZ MBY NAY MCX

TEST
FIGURE

LBX	NBY	MAZ
a	**b**	**c**

NCZ	NCY
d	**e**

4)

W	W	X	Y
F	G	H	F

TEST
FIGURE

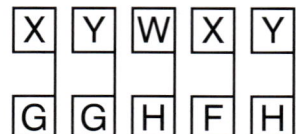

X	Y	W	X	Y
G	G	H	F	H
a	**b**	**c**	**d**	**e**

5)

LPFX MPGZ NQHZ MRHX

TEST
FIGURE

NPFX	NPGZ	NPFZ
a	**b**	**c**

MPFX	NRQZ
d	**e**

6)

TEST FIGURE

GN	FO	FM
a	**b**	**c**

GM	GF
d	**e**

FM   FN   GO

---

7)

TEST FIGURE

ZLQV	ANQU	ANPV
a	**b**	**c**

ZNQV	ZNRV
d	**e**

ZLPT   ZMPU   AMQV   ANRU

---

8)

TEST FIGURE

TPG	UQG	UPH
a	**b**	**c**

UQH	TQG
d	**e**

SPG   TQH   SQI   UPG

---

9)

TEST FIGURE

BJ	BM	AM
a	**b**	**c**

CL	CJ
d	**e**

AJ   BK   AL   CM

---

10)

TEST FIGURE

GXR	FWP	FXR
a	**b**	**c**

GWP	GXP
d	**e**

EVP   FVQ   GWQ   EXR

11)

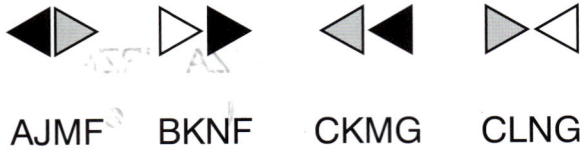

AJMF   BKNF   CKMG   CLNG

BJMF	AKMF	BJMG
a	**b**	**c**

BLNF	BJNG
d	**e**

---

12)

TEST FIGURE

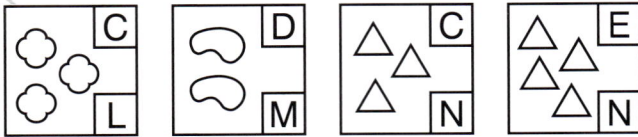

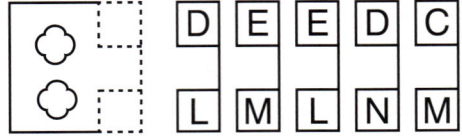

D	E	E	D	C
L	M	L	N	M
a	**b**	**c**	**d**	**e**

---

13)

TEST FIGURE

RCJO   SBKP   TBJQ   TCKP

TCKQ	SCKR	SBJP
a	**b**	**c**

SCKQ	SCJQ
d	**e**

---

14)

TEST FIGURE

WD   XE   YD   YF

XF	WE	WF
a	**b**	**c**

YD	XD
d	**e**

---

15)

TEST FIGURE

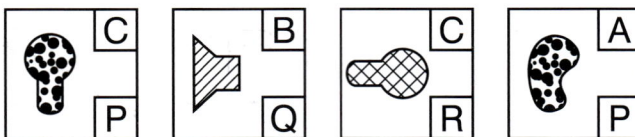

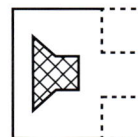

B	A	B	C	Q
P	Q	R	Q	R
a	**b**	**c**	**d**	**e**

16)

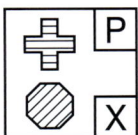

HQZA   IRZB   HSYA   JQYB

TEST FIGURE

JSZB	JRZA	JRYA
a	**b**	**c**

HQZA	IRZA
d	**e**

---

17)

XEJ   YFJ   ZEK   YEJ

TEST FIGURE

XFJ	ZFJ	XFK
a	**b**	**c**

ZEJ	XEK
d	**e**

---

18)

CJS   BJT   AKU   CLV

TEST FIGURE

BLS	CKT	BLV
a	**b**	**c**

ALV	BJS
d	**e**

---

19)

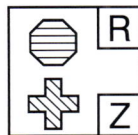

AH   BI   AI   CJ

TEST FIGURE

BJ	CH	AJ
a	**b**	**c**

CI	BH
d	**e**

---

20)

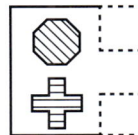

TEST FIGURE

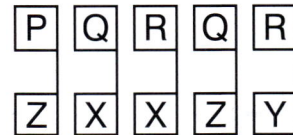

P	Q	R	Q	R
Z	X	X	Z	Y
a	**b**	**c**	**d**	**e**

Score

Chapter Nineteen
ANALOGIES
1. Level One

On the left there are two figures with an arrow between them. Decide how the second figure is related to the first. Decide which of the five figures to the right of the arrow goes with the **third** figure to **make a pair** like the two figures on the left.

Example

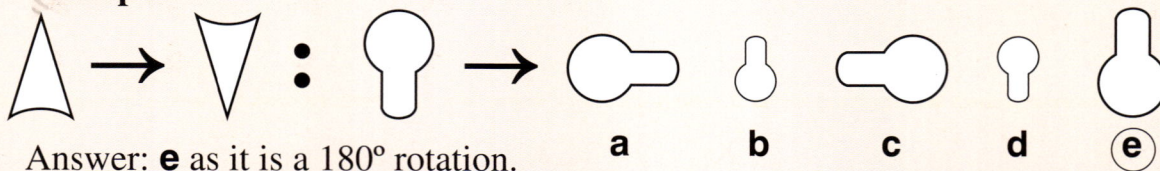

Answer: **e** as it is a 180° rotation.

a   b   c   d   (e)

Exercise 19: 1 Which figure completes the analogy?

1)

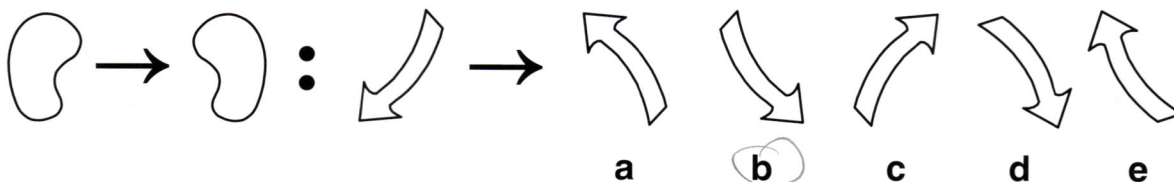

a   (b)   c   d   e

2)

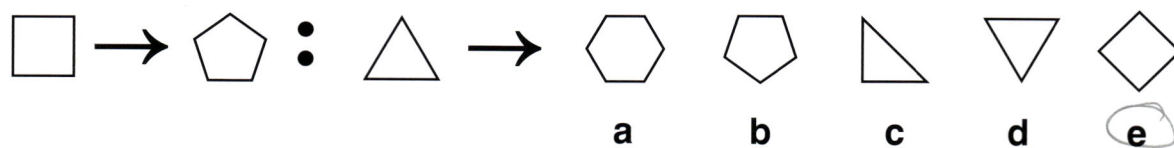

a   b   c   d   (e)

3)

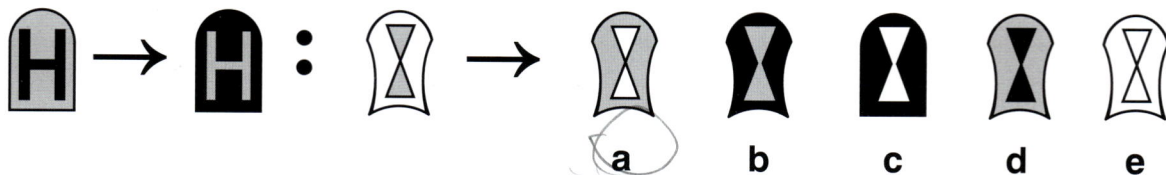

(a)   b   c   d   e

4)

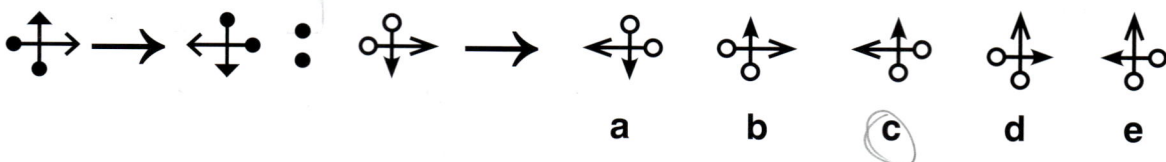

a   b   (c)   d   e

5)

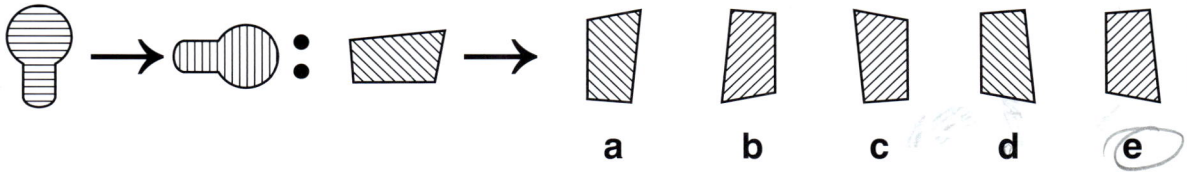

        a   b   c   d   e

6)

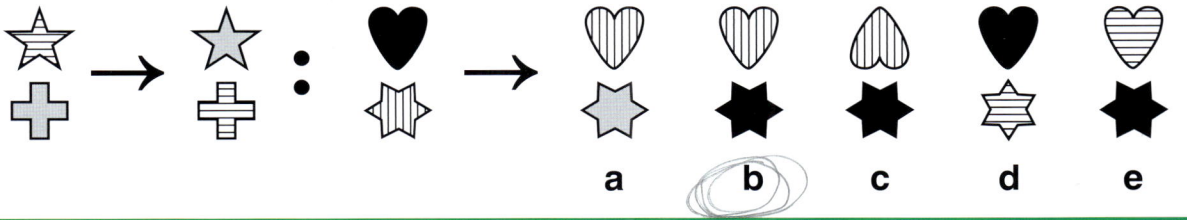

        a   b   c   d   e

7)

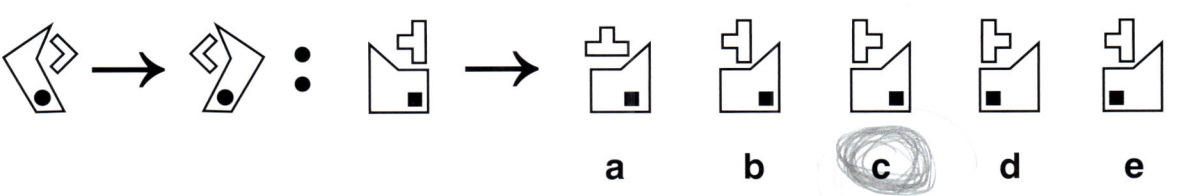

        a   b   c   d   e

8)

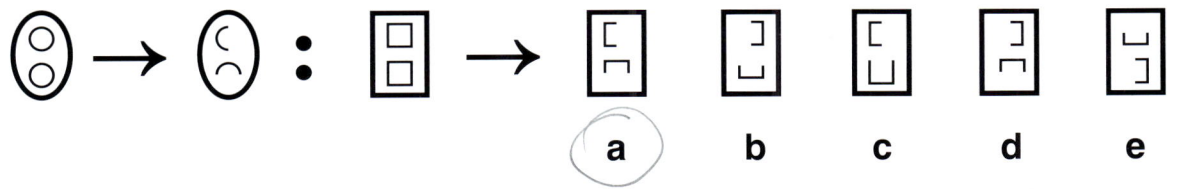

        a   b   c   d   e

9)

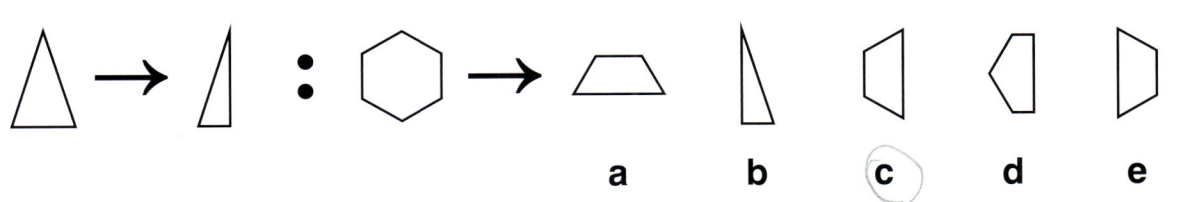

        a   b   c   d   e

10)

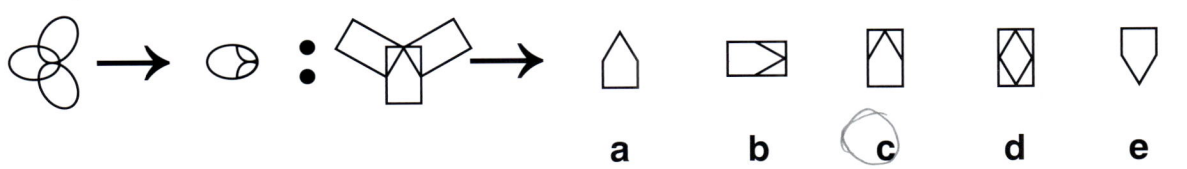

        a   b   c   d   e

11)

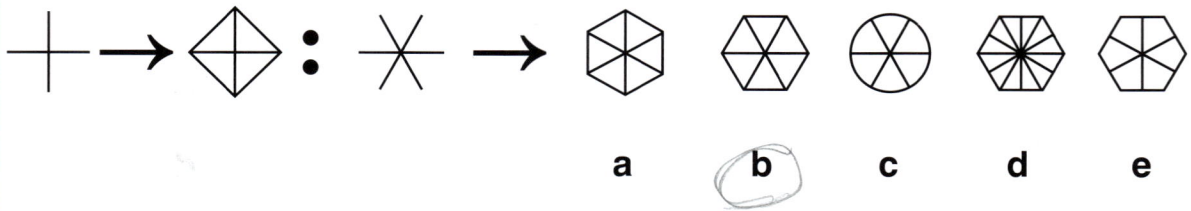

a   **b**   c   d   e

12)

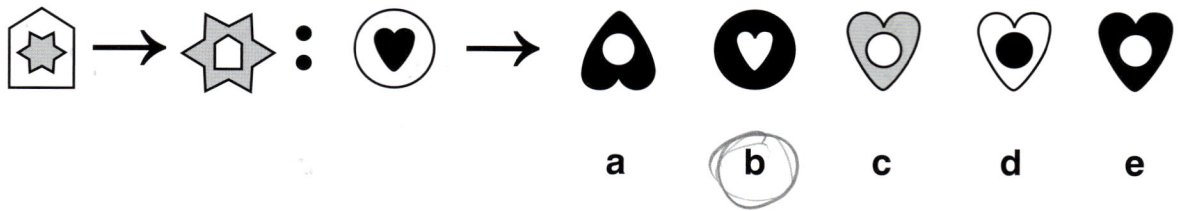

a   **b**   c   d   e

13)

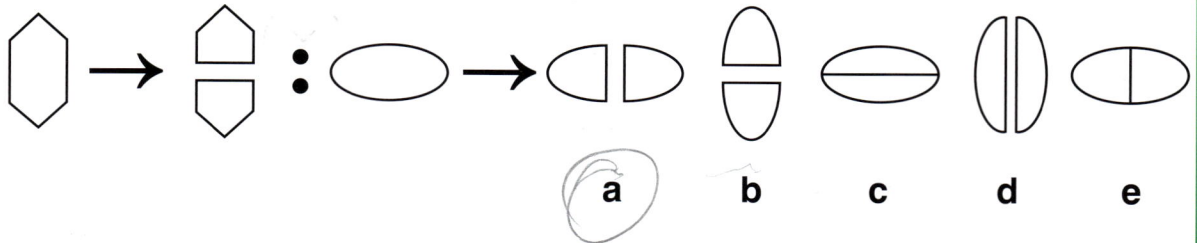

a   b   c   d   e

14)

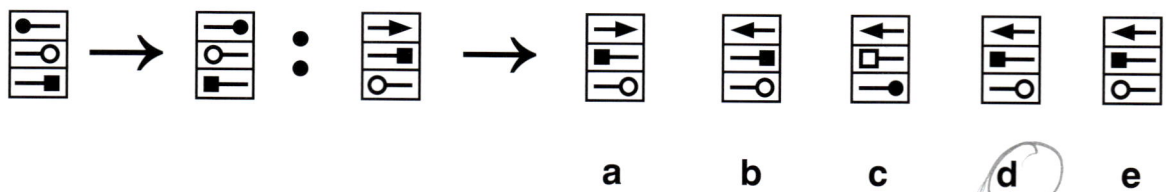

a   b   c   **d**   e

15)

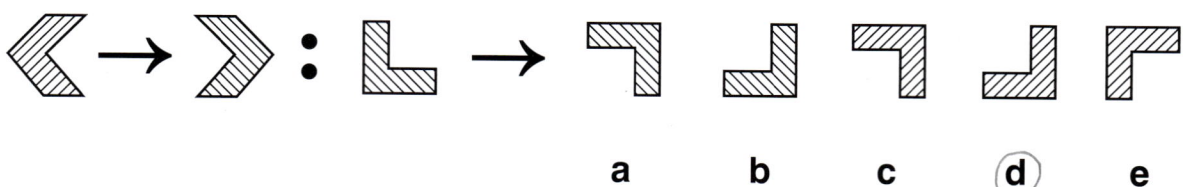

a   b   c   **d**   e

16)

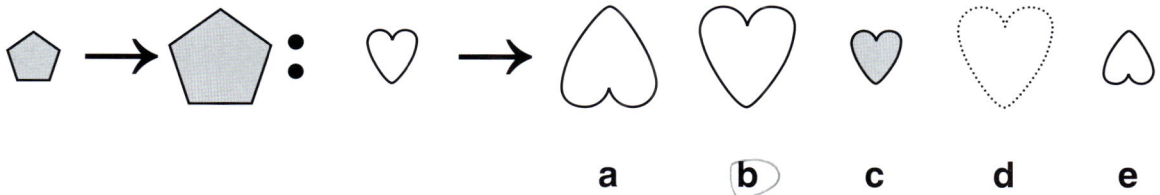

                             a   b   c   d   e

17)

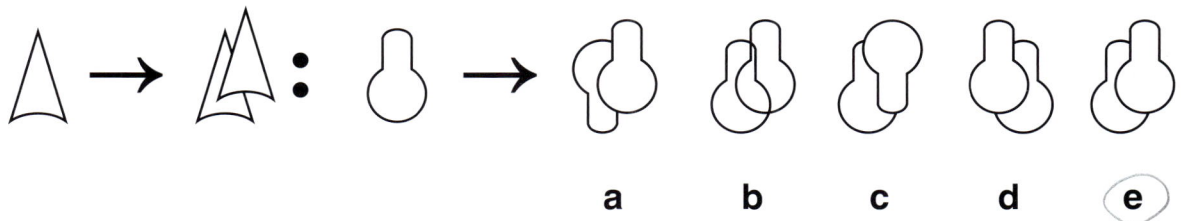

                             a   b   c   d   e

18)

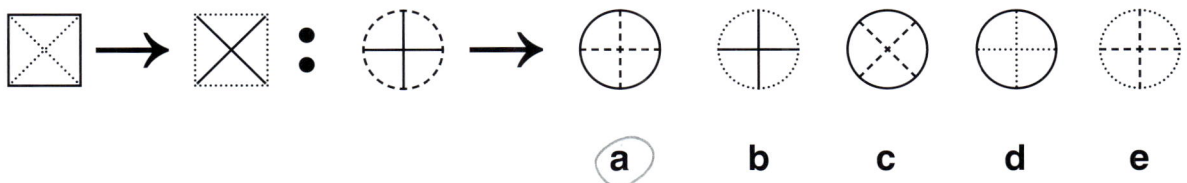

                             a   b   c   d   e

19)

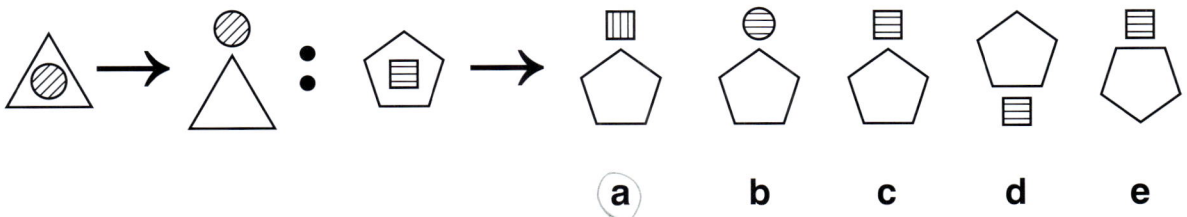

                             a   b   c   d   e

20)

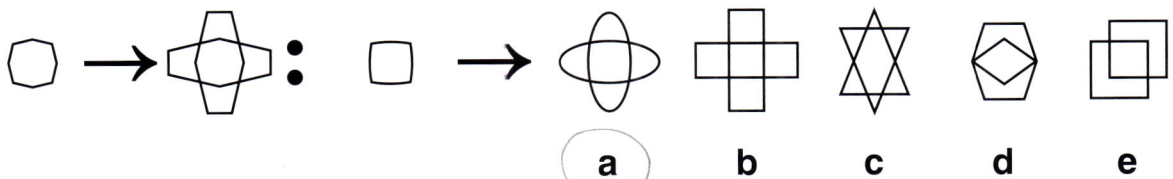

                             a   b   c   d   e

Score

2. Level Two

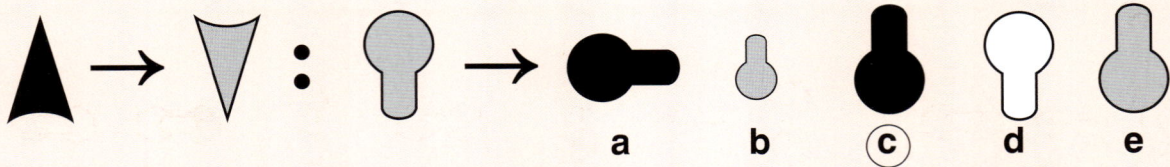
Exercise 19: 2 Which figure completes the analogy?

1)

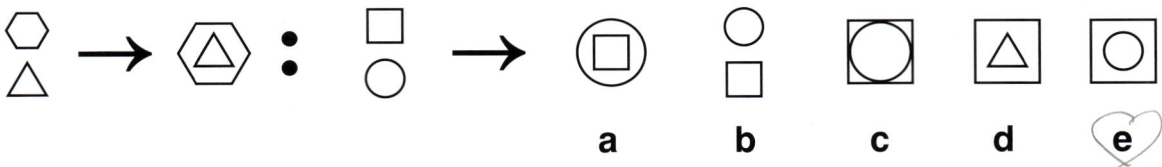

2)

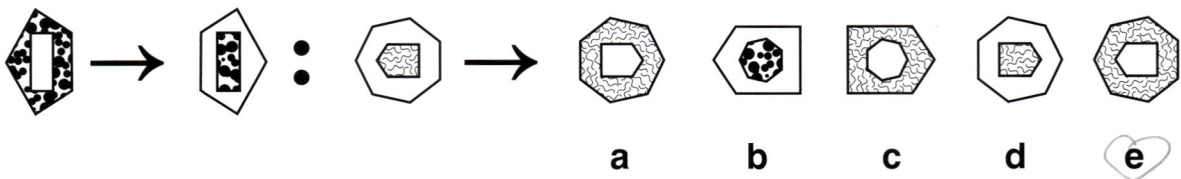

3)

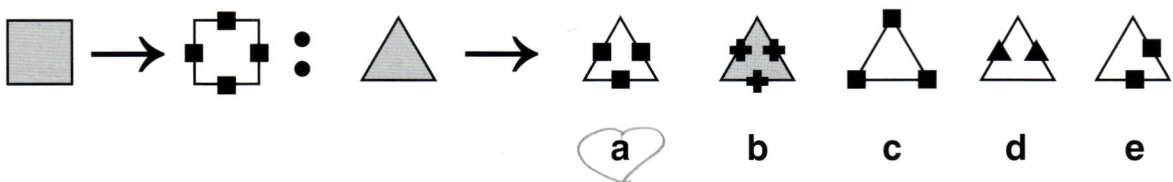

4)

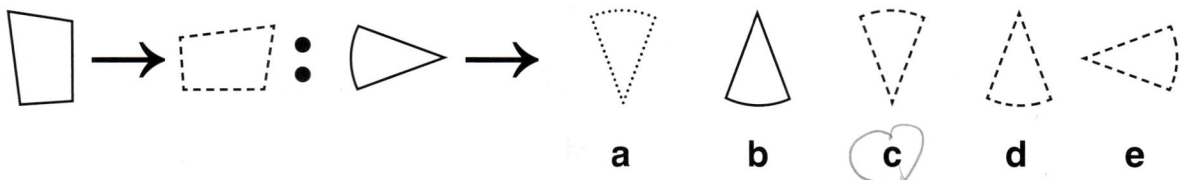

5)

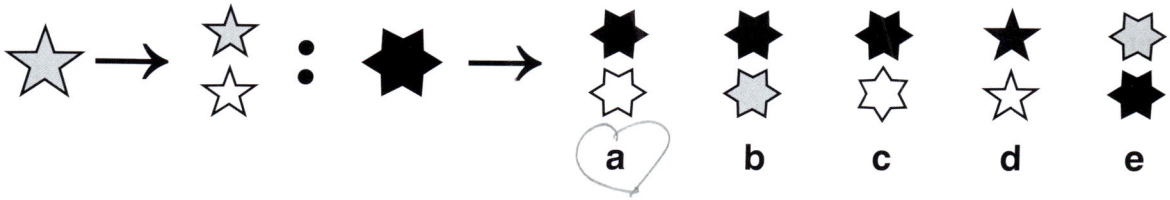

6)

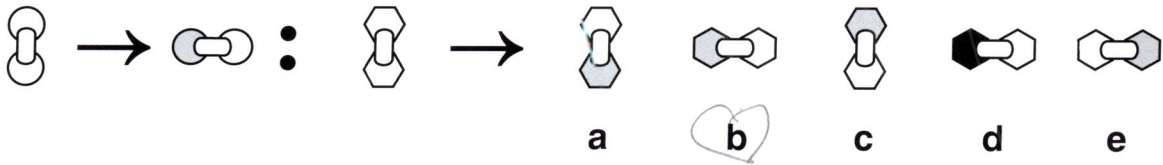

7)

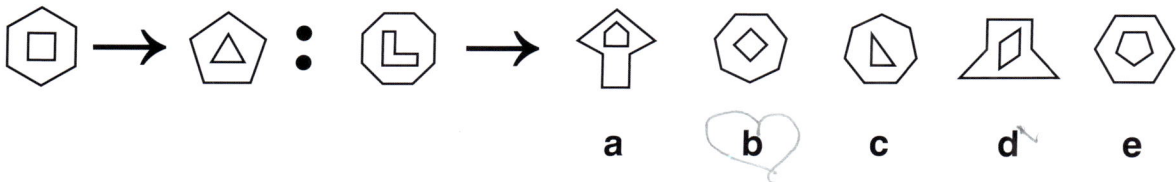

8)

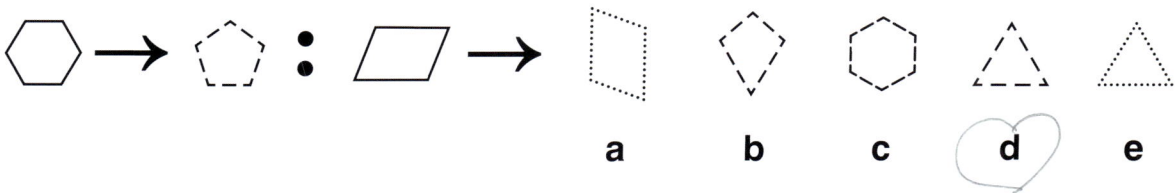

9)

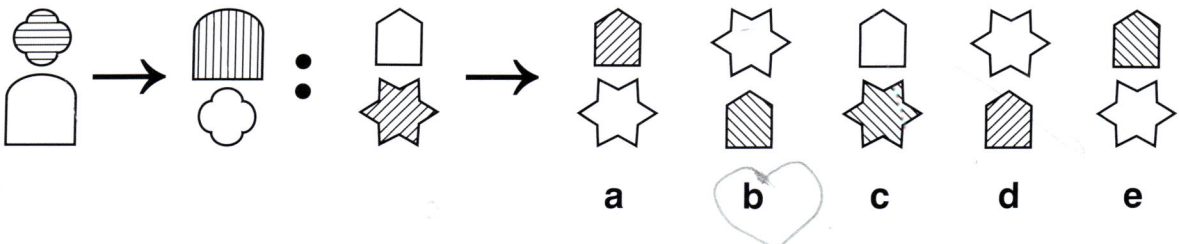

10)

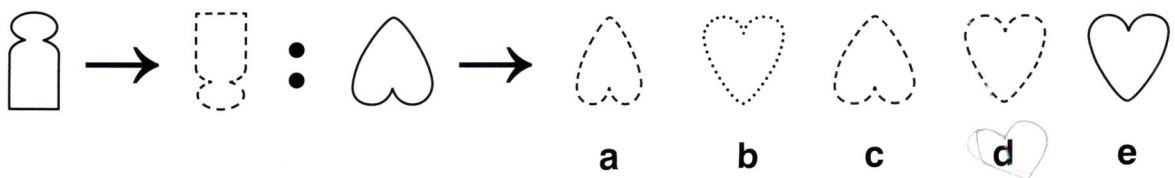

11)

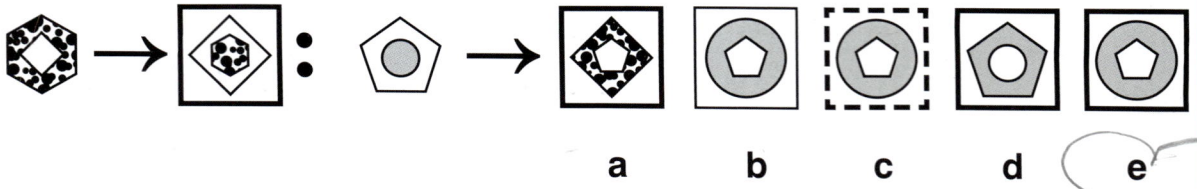

a   b   c   d   e

12)

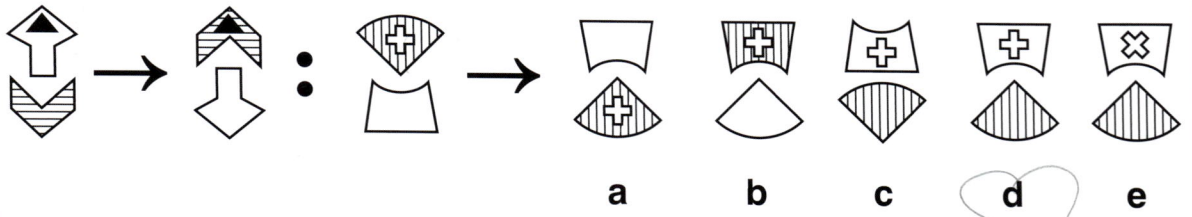

a   b   c   d   e

13)

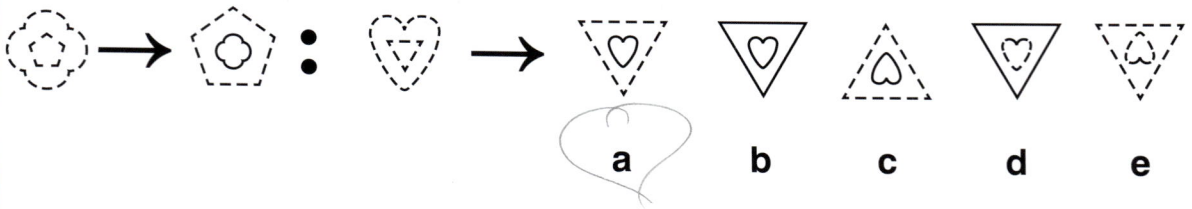

a   b   c   d   e

14)

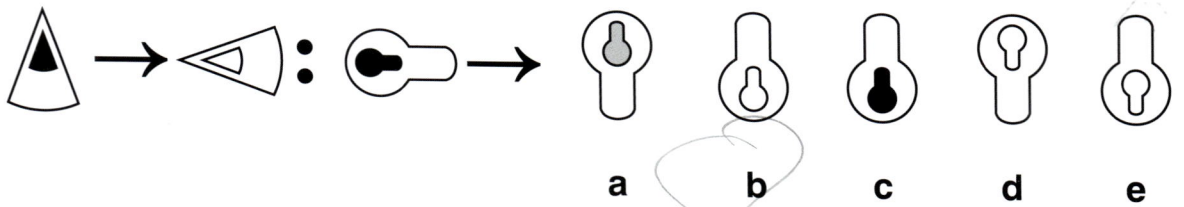

a   b   c   d   e

15)

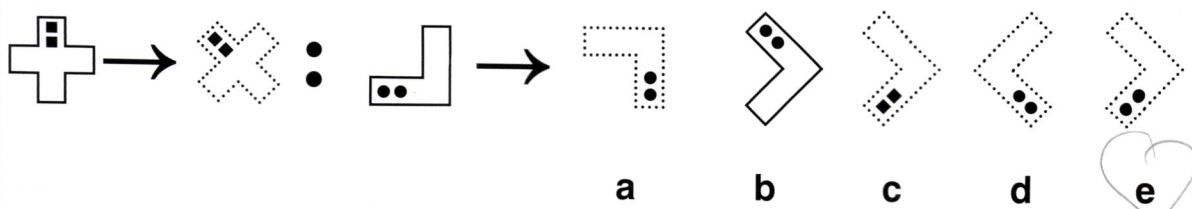

a   b   c   d   e

16)

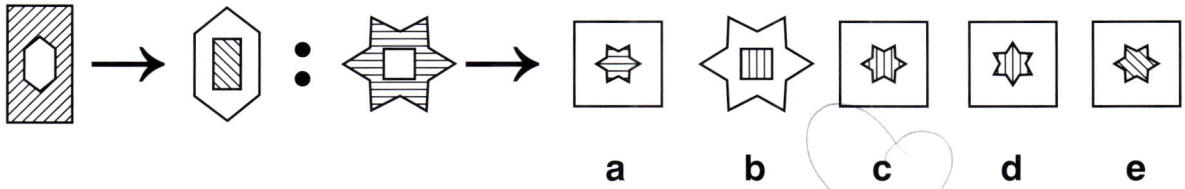

a   b   c   d   e

17)

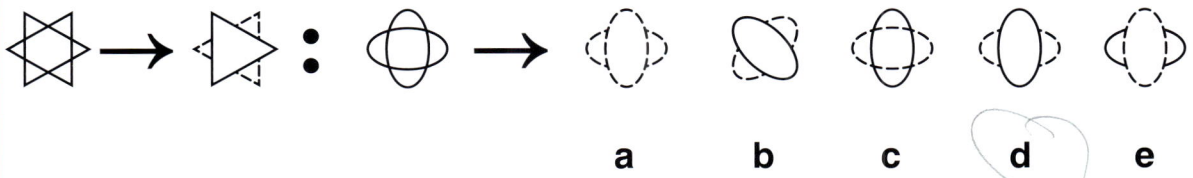

a   b   c   d   e

18)

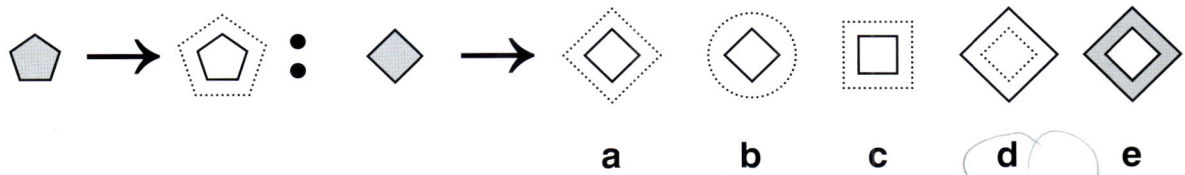

a   b   c   d   e

19)

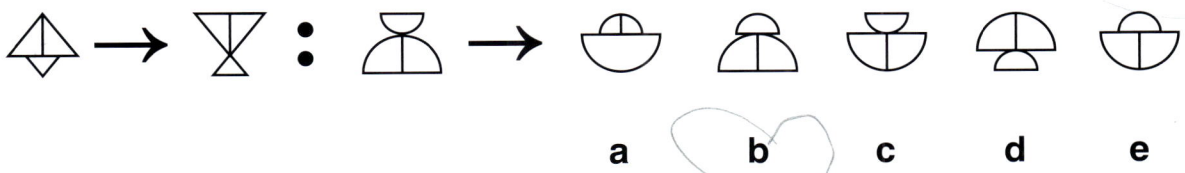

a   b   c   d   e

20)

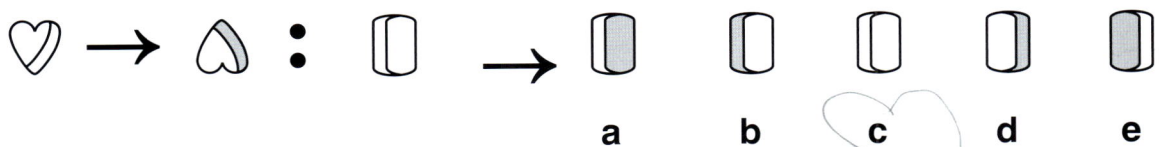

a   b   c   d   e

Score

3. Level Three

Example

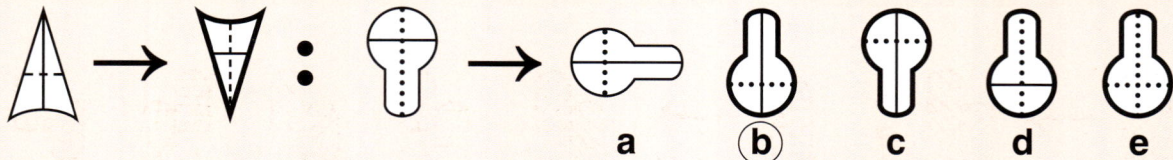

a   **b**   c   d   e

Answer: **b** as it is a 180° rotation, the lines have been reversed and the shape has a Thick Solid Line.

Exercise 19: 3 Which figure completes the analogy?

1)

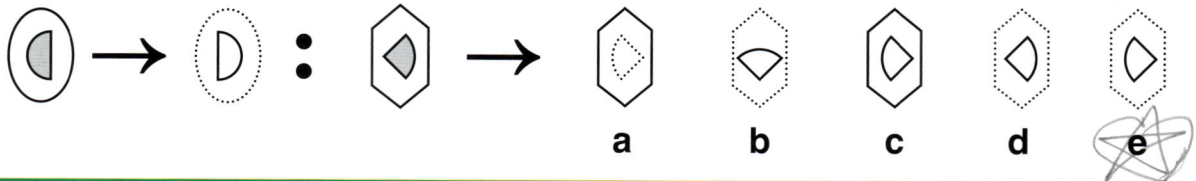

a   b   c   d   e

2)

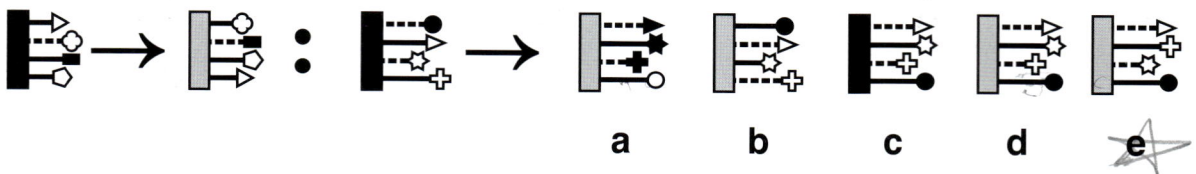

a   b   c   d   e

3)

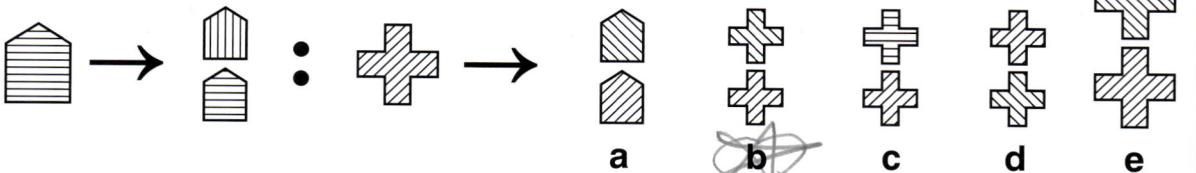

a   b   c   d   e

4)

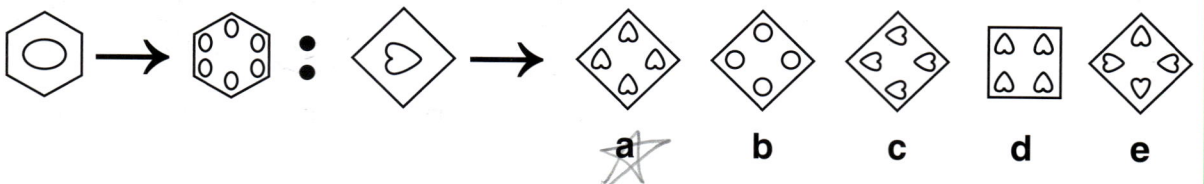

a   b   c   d   e

5)

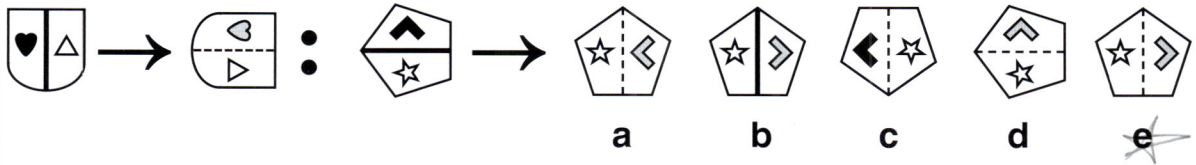

a b c d e

6)

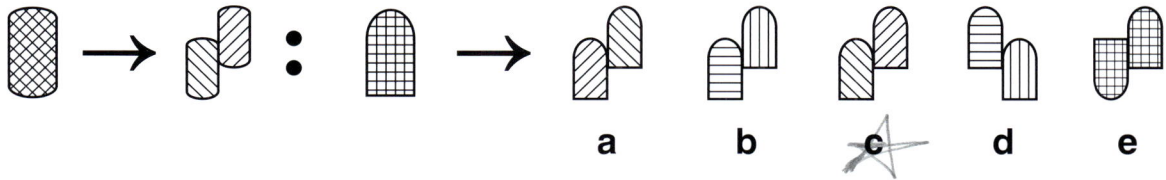

a b c d e

7)

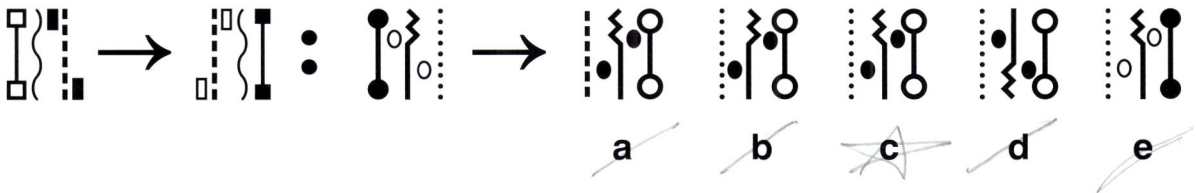

a b c d e

8)

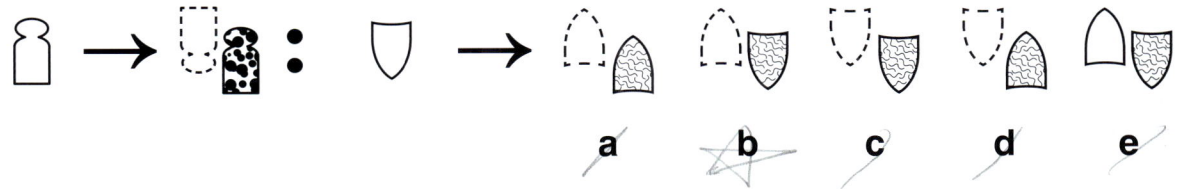

a b c d e

9)

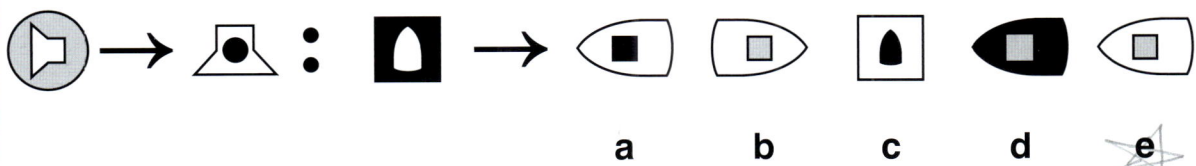

a b c d e

10)

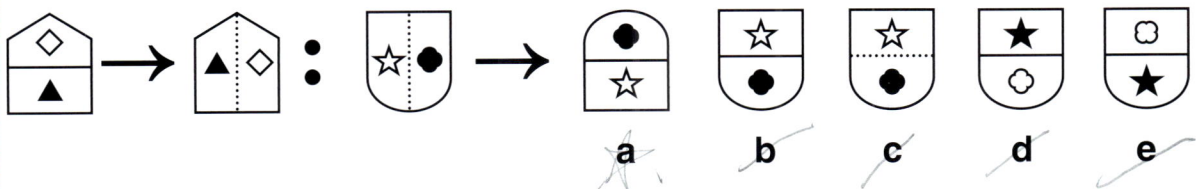

a b c d e

11)

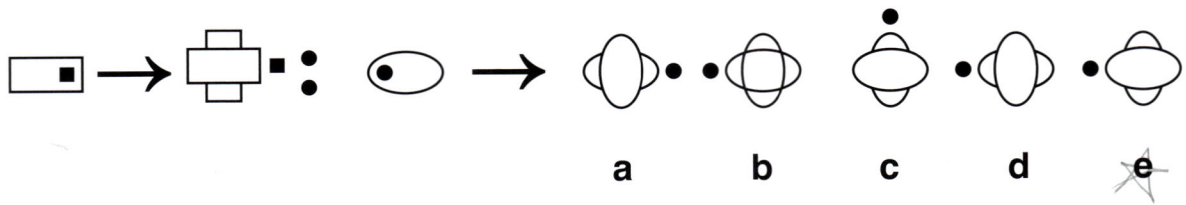

a   b   c   d   e

12)

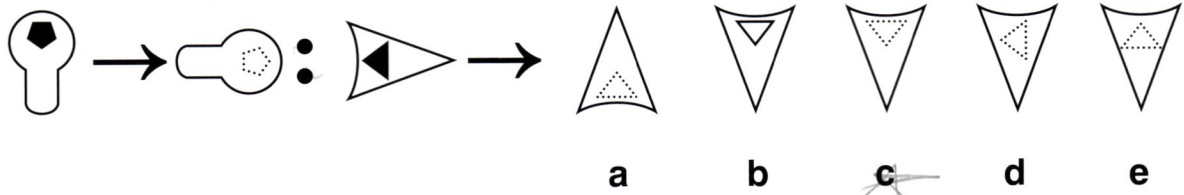

a   b   c   d   e

13)

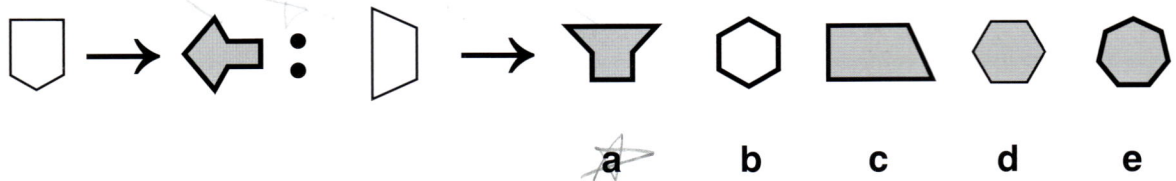

a   b   c   d   e

14)

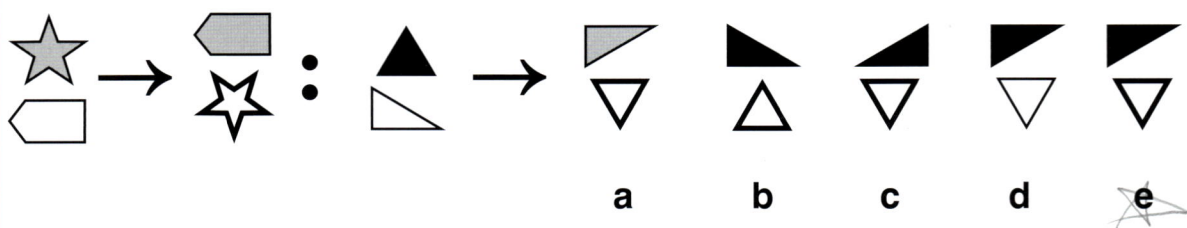

a   b   c   d   e

15)

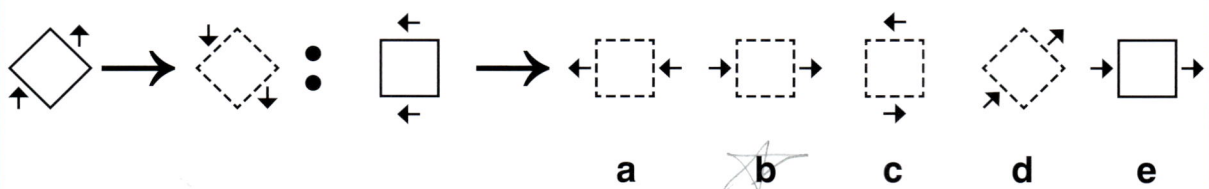

a   b   c   d   e

16)

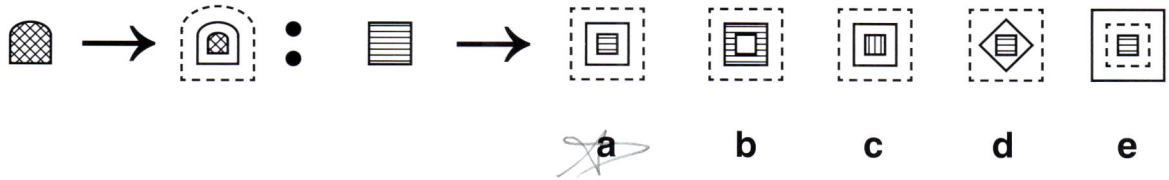

a b c d e

17)

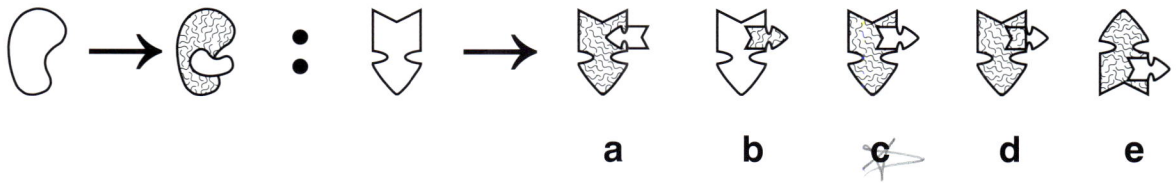

a b c d e

18)

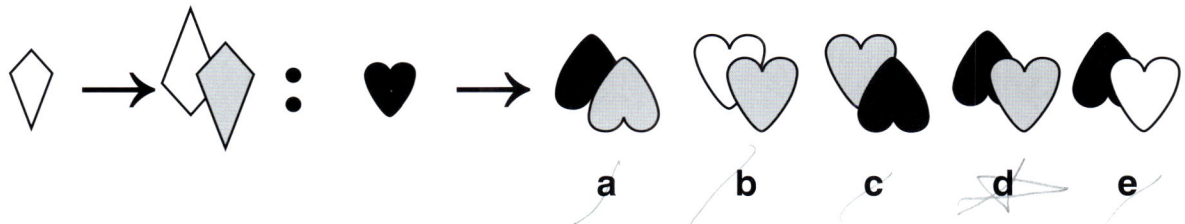

a b c d e

19)

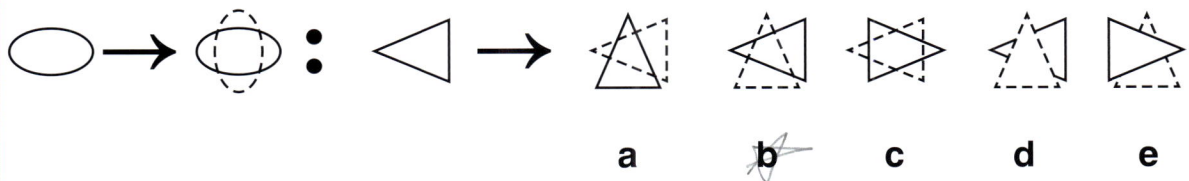

a b c d e

20)

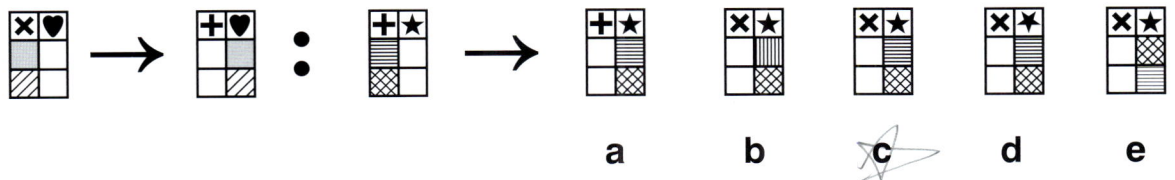

a b c d e

Score

4. Levels Four & Five

On the left are two figures with an arrow between them. Decide how the second figure is related to the first. Decide which of the five figures to the right of the arrow goes with the **third** figure to **make a pair** like the two figures on the left.

Example

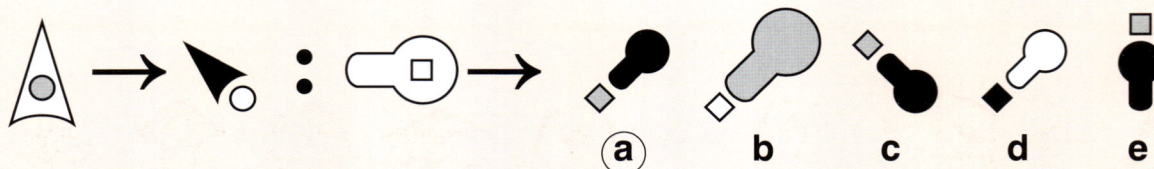

Answer: **a** as it is a 45° anticlockwise rotation, the shapes have been reduced in size, the fills of both shapes have been reversed and the square is no longer enclosed.

Exercise 19: 4 Which figure completes the analogy?

1)

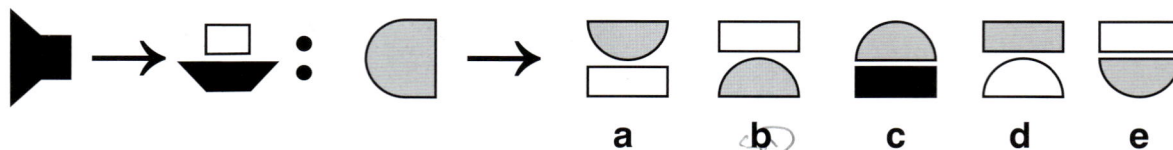

2)

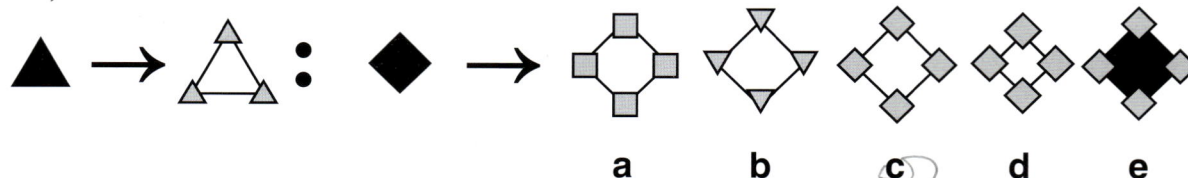

3)

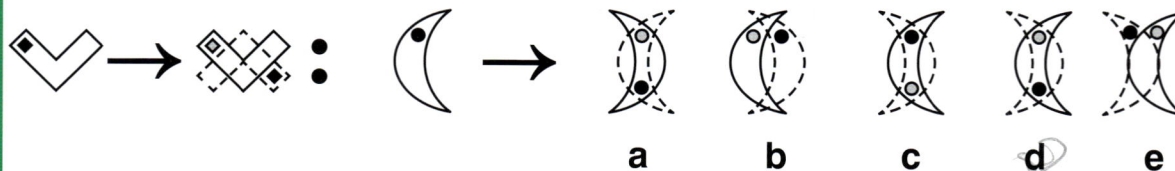

4)

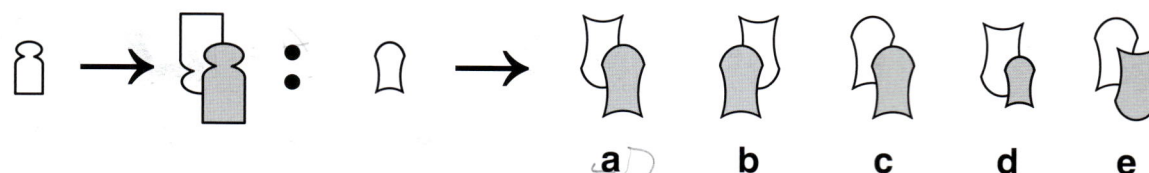

5)

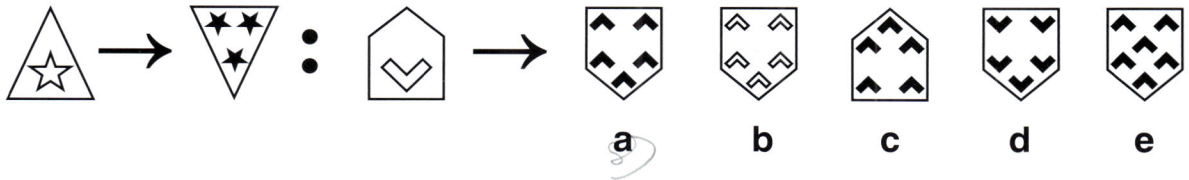

6)

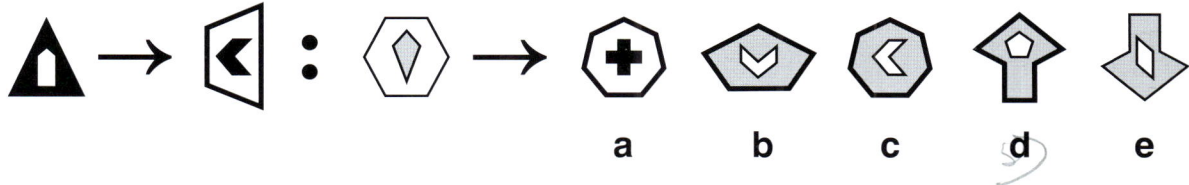

7)

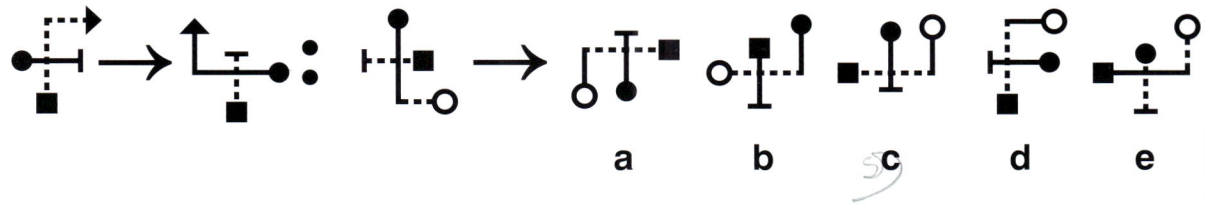

8)

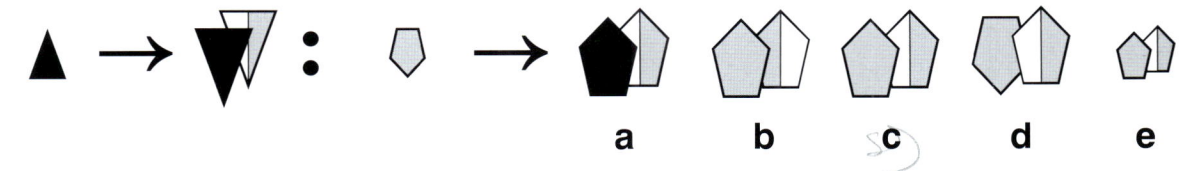

9)

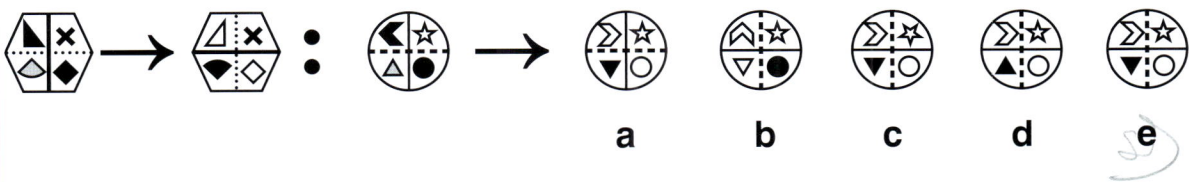

10)

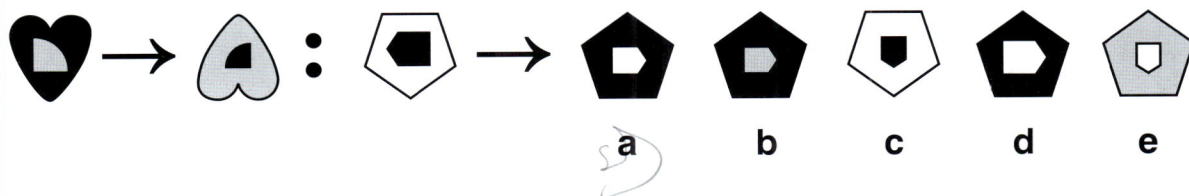

11)

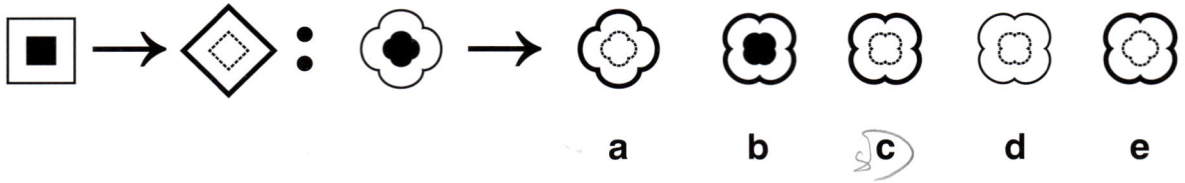

a   b   **c**   d   e

12)

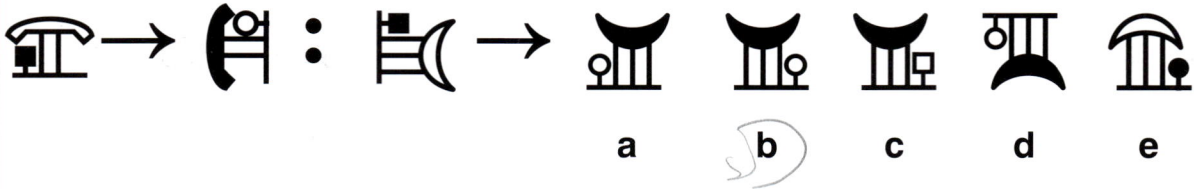

a   **b**   c   d   e

13)

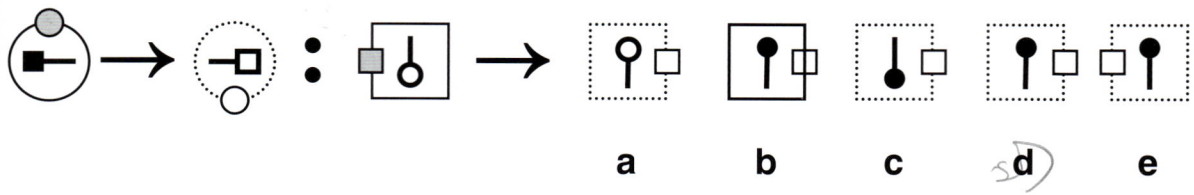

a   b   c   **d**   e

14)

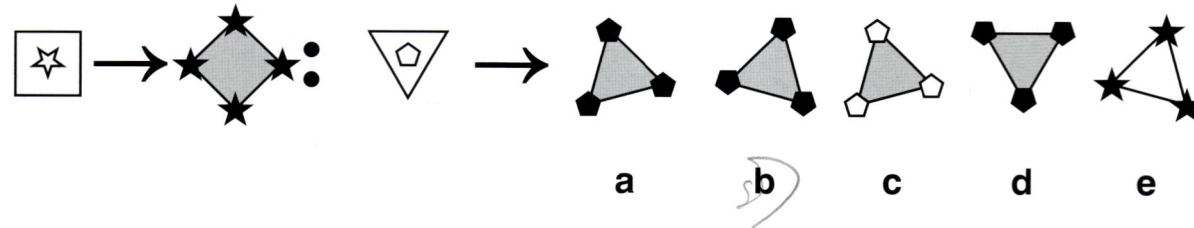

a   **b**   c   d   e

15)

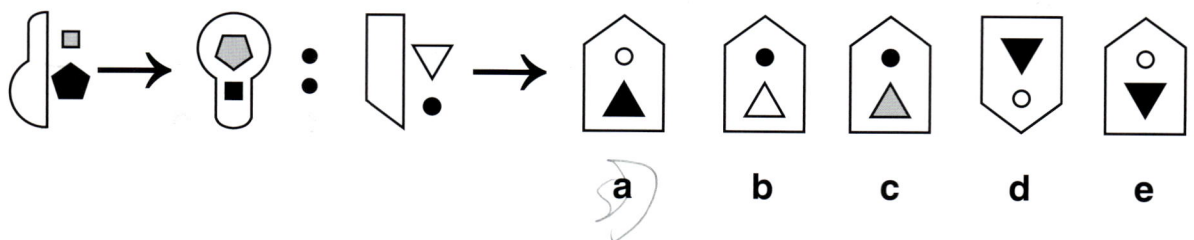

a   b   c   d   e

16)

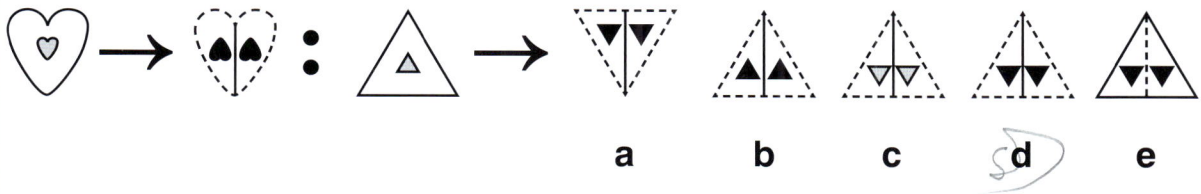

a   b   c   d   e

17)

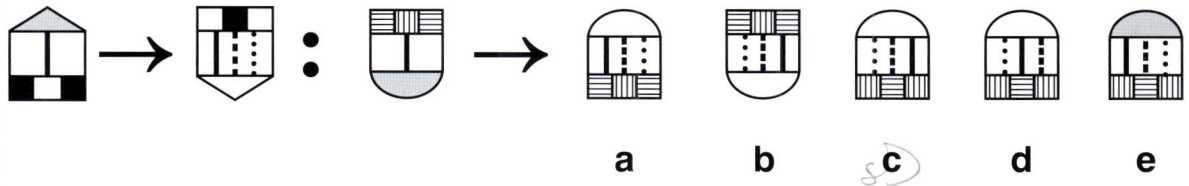

a   b   c   d   e

18)

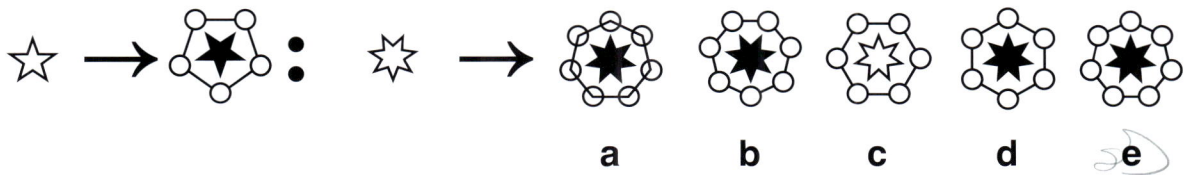

a   b   c   d   e

19)

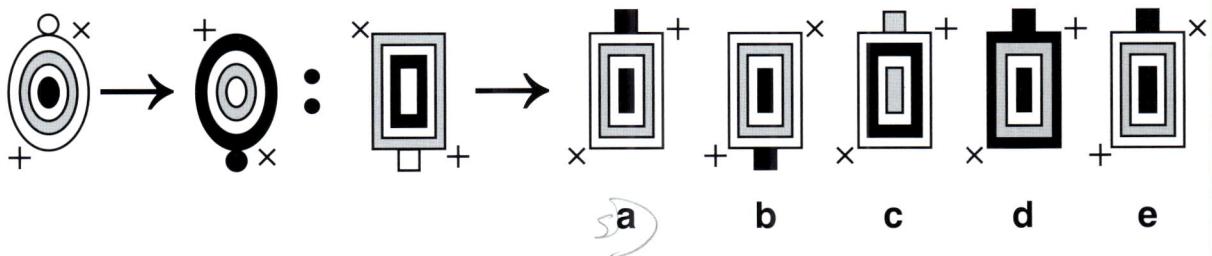

a   b   c   d   e

20)

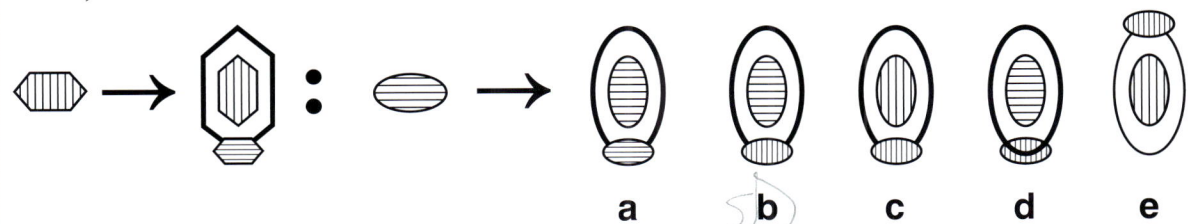

a   b   c   d   e

Score

5. Mixed Levels

Exercise 19: 5 Which figure completes the analogy?

1)

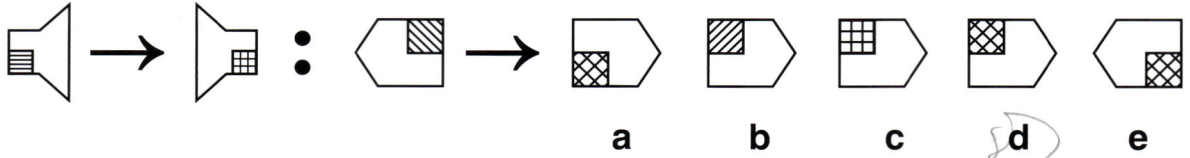

      a   **b**   **c**   **d**   **e**

2)

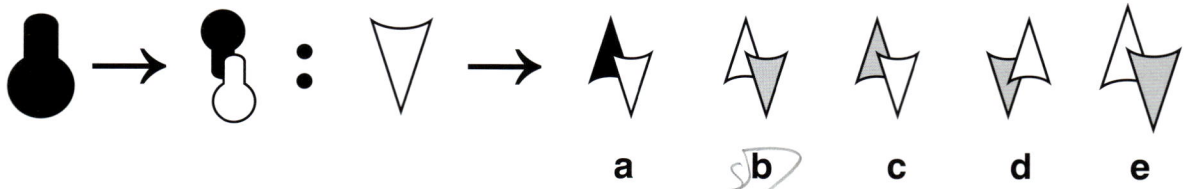

      a   **b**   **c**   **d**   **e**

3)

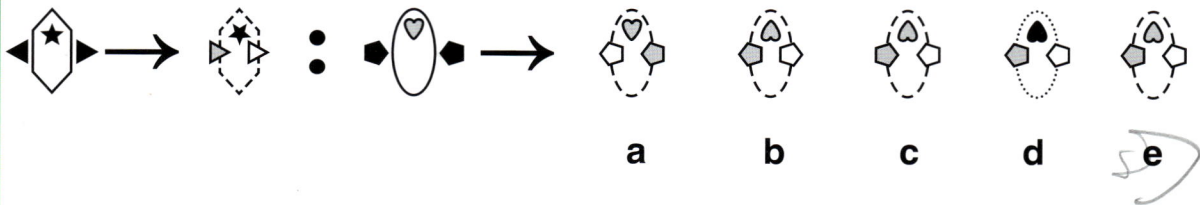

      a   **b**   **c**   **d**   **e**

4)

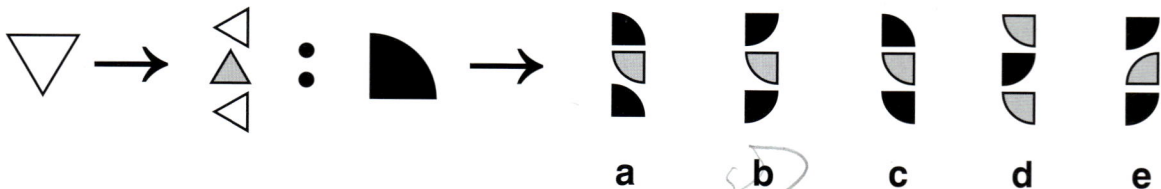

      a   **b**   **c**   **d**   **e**

5)

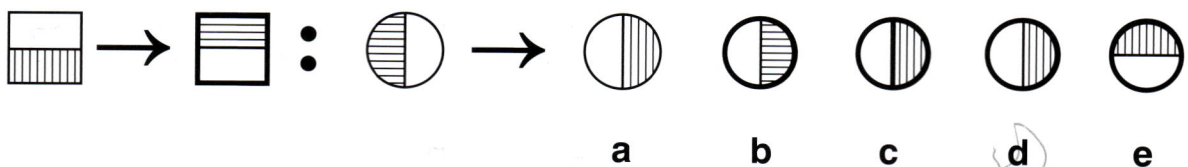

      a   **b**   **c**   **d**   **e**

6)

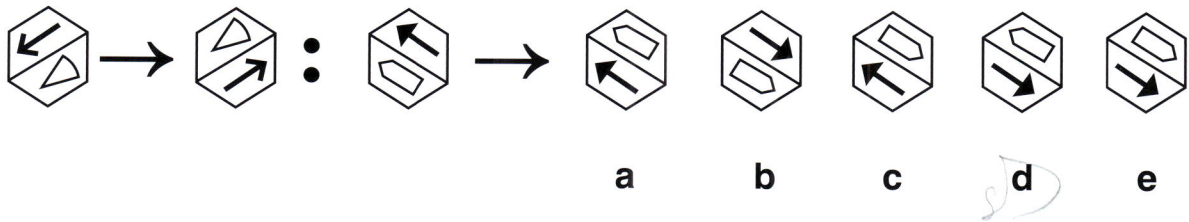

a   b   c   d   e

7)

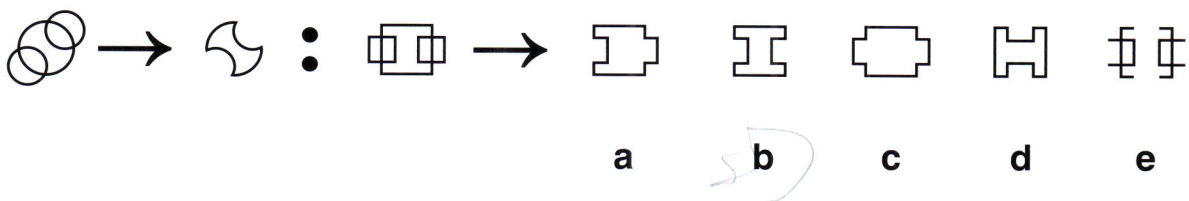

a   b   c   d   e

8)

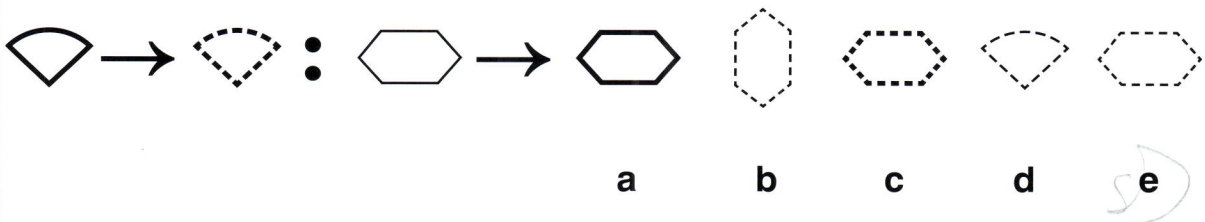

a   b   c   d   e

9)

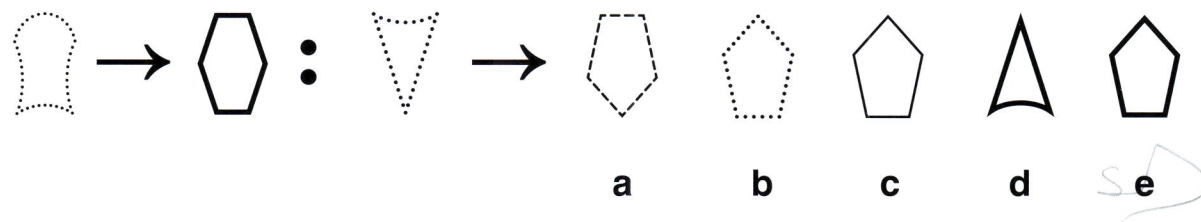

a   b   c   d   e

10)

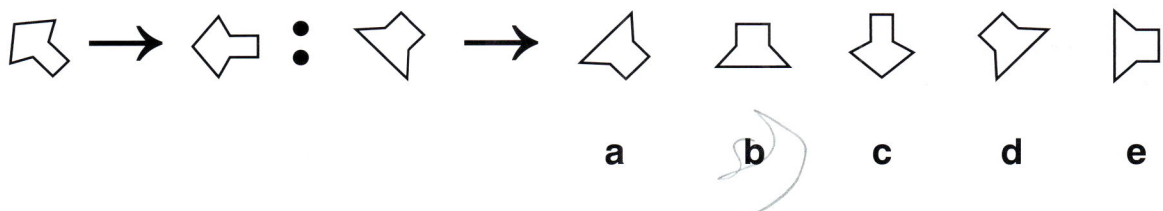

a   b   c   d   e

11)

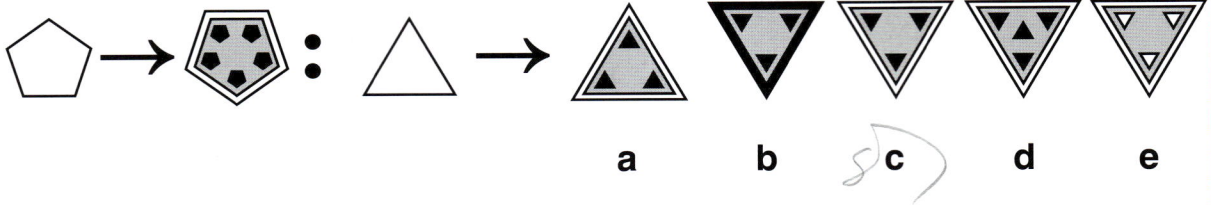

a b c d e

12)

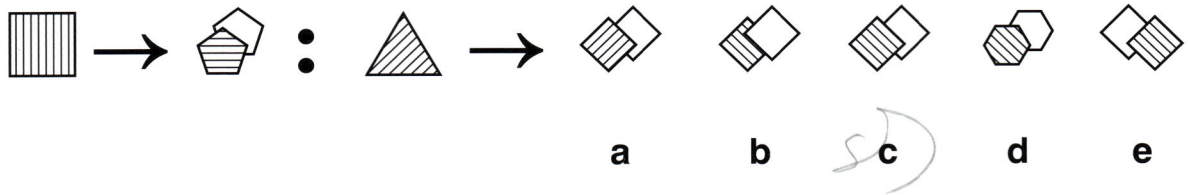

a b c d e

13)

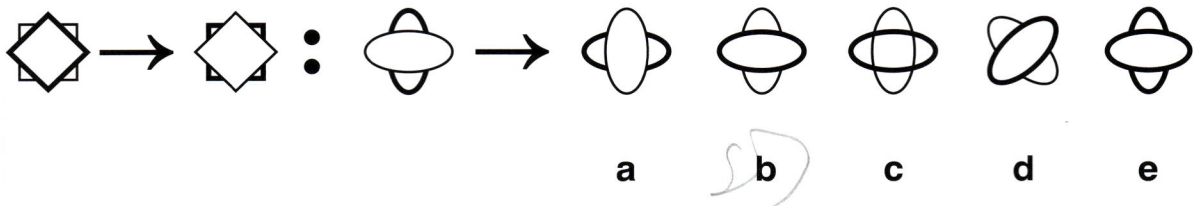

a b c d e

14)

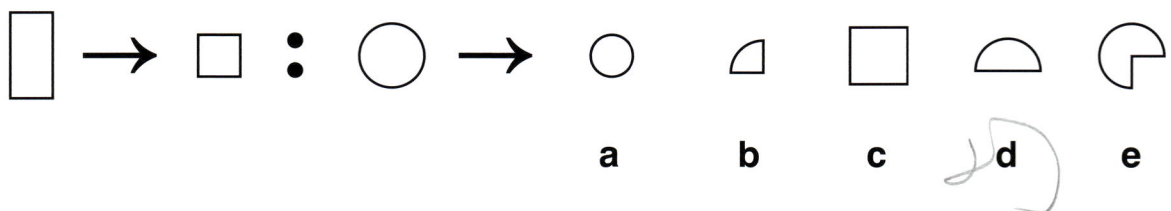

a b c d e

15)

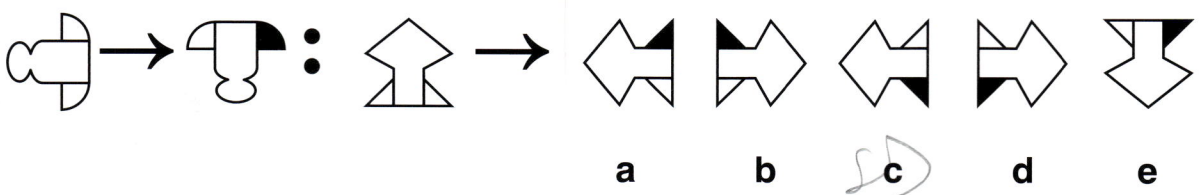

a b c d e

16)

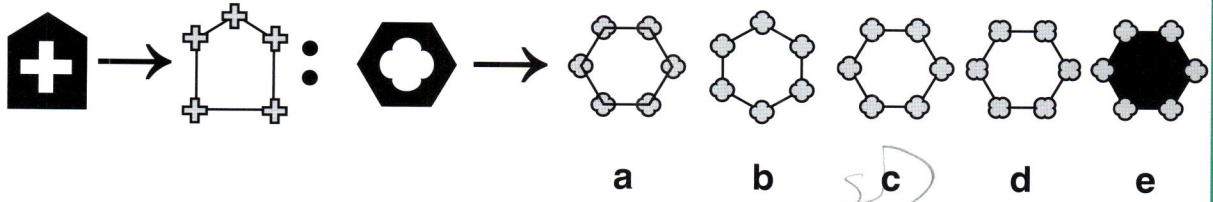

                                  a   **b**   **c**   **d**   **e**

17)

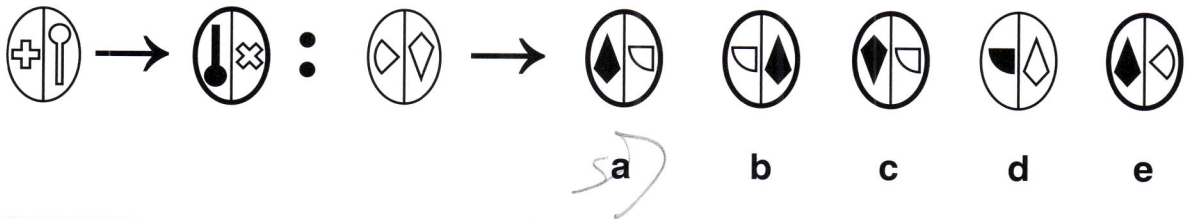

                                  a   **b**   **c**   **d**   **e**

18)

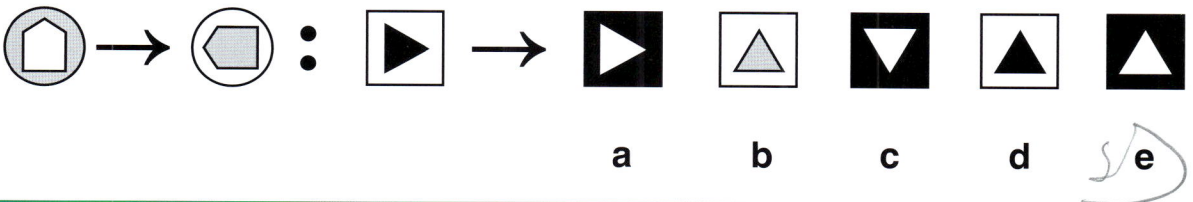

                                  a   **b**   **c**   **d**   **e**

19)

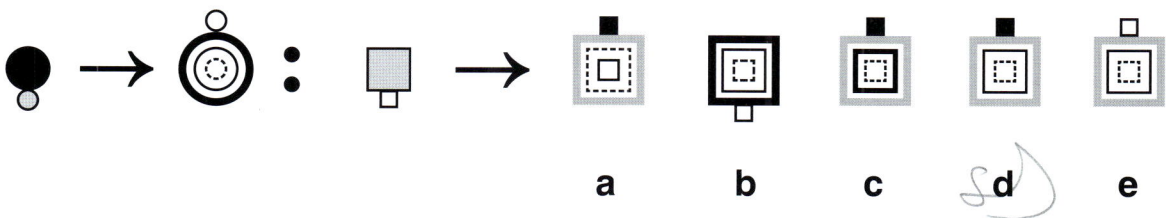

                                  a   **b**   **c**   **d**   **e**

20)

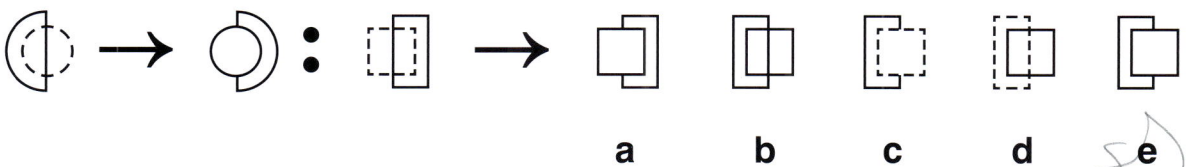

                                  a   **b**   **c**   **d**   **e**

Score

Answers

Chapter Seventeen

Odd One Out

Exercise 17: 1

1) **d** - The Circle is not enclosed on the left of the Semi-circle.
2) **b** - The two shapes are not perpendicular to each other.
3) **c** - The figure is not the same rotation as the other figures.
4) **e** - The fill is not Left Slant Lined.
5) **b** - The diagonal fill is not Right Slant Lined Fill.
6) **c** - The shape does not have four sides.
7) **a** - The shape does not have a Grey or Black Fill.
8) **b** - The two shapes in the figure are not the same.
9) **a** - The fill is not Left Slant Lined.
10) **c** - The middle shape is not overlaying the outer shape with a Solid Outline.
11) **e** - The Arrow does not have the same slant as the other Arrows.
12) **d** - The Arrow does not point clockwise.
13) **e** - There are not two vertical H shapes.
14) **a** - The shape does not have a Shaded Fill.
15) **a** - The figure does not have only one Arrowhead.
16) **c** - The two shapes in the figure are not the same.
17) **b** - The two shapes in the figure are not the same.
18) **e** - The lines do not meet in the centre of the Circle.
19) **c** - The enclosed shape is not an overlay.
20) **b** - The figure does not have only one line of symmetry.

Exercise 17: 2

1) **a** - The number of Crosses is not equal to one more than the number of sides of the shape.
2) **a** - The figure does not contain three long lines and one short line.
3) **b** - The two shapes do not face in opposite directions.
4) **e** - The smaller Rectangle does not have a White Fill.

5) **b** - The order of outlines is not Thick, Thin, Thick.
6) **e** - The number of enclosed Circles is not equal to the number of sides of the outer shape.
7) **b** - The Arrow is not pointing upwards.
8) **d** - The Circle with a Grey Fill is not overlaying one of the Circles with a White Fill.
9) **e** - The enclosed Square is not the same rotation as in the other figures.
10) **b** - When positioned vertically, the shape does not have a Vertical Lined Fill.
11) **e** - The figure does not contain 3 Squares and 2 Crosses.
12) **b** - The figure does not include a shape with a Dashed Outline.
13) **e** - The enclosed line is not a line of symmetry.
14) **e** - The Circle with a Black Fill is not on its own.
15) **a** - The shape does not have an odd number of sides.
16) **d** - The shape is not a rotation of the other shapes.
17) **b** - When rotated so the arrow is pointing upwards, the arrow is not on the left of any vertical Ellipses and on the right of any horizontal Ellipses.
18) **c** - The number of sides is increased by 1, not 2.
19) **c** - The Triangles enclosed in the linkage do not have a White Fill.
20) **b** - The shape on the right of the figure is not a reflection of the shape on the left.

Exercise 17: 3

1) **c** - The enclosed shape is not a different rotation to the outer shape.
2) **e** - The Lined Fill is not Vertical or Diagonal.
3) **b** - The Arrowhead is not open.
4) **e** - The large shape does not have five sides.
5) **b** - The outer shape of the figure is not a rotation of the other figures.

Answers

6) **c** - There is not only one point between the two Squares.

7) **c** - The small shape with a Black Fill is not with the large shape with a Lattice Fill.

8) **c** - The Arrowhead is not closed.

9) **a** - The number of enclosed Circles does not equal the number of sides of the outer shape.

10) **b** - The fill of the enclosed linkages is not the same.

11) **d** - There are not more Heart Shapes with a White Fill than with a Black Fill.

12) **c** - One of the Squares does not have the same fill as the enclosed Triangle. The Square with the White Fill is not on the left.

13) **a** - The Triangles with Grey and White Fills are not the same rotation as in the other figures.

14) **e** - The Circle is not outside of the shape.

15) **e** - The two shapes do not face in opposite directions.

16) **b** - The Grey Fill is not on the outer sections.

17) **d** - The Ellipse does not have a White or Black Fill.

18) **c** - The line with a White Circle ending is not long.

19) **b** - The number of lines is not equal to the number of shapes on each line.

20) **d** - The number of sides does not total 8.

Exercise 17: 4

1) **a** - The Circle does not enclose three shapes.

2) **d** - The figure does not have a Black Fill.

3) **b** - The line across the middle of the shape is not a line of symmetry.

4) **d** - The Sector does not point clockwise.

5) **c** - The Circle outside the Triangle is not on the edge of the Triangle.

6) **b** - The lines are not Thick.

7) **a** - The Circle is not on a point.

8) **c** - The Star does not face upwards.

9) **e** - The Arrow does not point between the Circle and the Square.

10) **b** - The figure does not have a Black Fill.

11) **b** - The number of sides of the enclosed shape is not one more than the number of sides of the outer shape.

12) **c** - The Wizard's Hat Shape does not point to the large section of the Triangle.

13) **a** - The number of shapes with a Black Fill is not the same as the number of sides of the shapes.

14) **e** - The outer shape does not have a line of symmetry.

15) **d** - The figure does not have two different fills.

16) **a** - The enclosed Flower Shape is not a different rotation to the outer Flower Shape.

17) **c** - The Circle is not enclosed in the larger section of the Bean Shape.

18) **d** - The Lined Fill is not Vertical or Horizontal.

19) **b** - The Triangle is not the same rotation as the others.

20) **c** - The number of Circles is not one less than the number of sides of the other shape.

Exercise 17: 5

1) **b** - The number of Moon Shapes is not equal to the number of Shield Shapes.

2) **c** - There is no Circle with a Black Fill.

3) **e** - The large shape does not overlay one of the small shapes.

4) **c** - The enclosed shapes do not have a different orientation from the shapes outside the larger shape.

5) **e** - The Circle with the Black Fill is not on the left.

6) **d** - The figure does not have five sections.

7) **e** - The enclosed shapes are not the same as the outer shape.

8) **a** - The small Moon Shape does not have a White Fill.

9) **c** - The Lined Fill is not Vertical or Horizontal.

10) **a** - The horizontal line is not Thick.

11) **e** - The shape with a Black Fill is not a different rotation to the outer shape.

12) **a** - The figure does not have a line of symmetry.

13) **e** - The figure is not a rotation of the other figures.

14) **d** - The Circles do not have a Black or White Fill.

15) **b** - The General Quadrilateral is not the same rotation as the others.

16) **a** - The enclosed lines do not join two inner points.

17) **d** - The figure does not have a Curved shape.

18) **a** - The figure does not consist of Straight-edged shapes.

19) **e** - The Star does not have a Grey or Black Fill.

20) **d** - When the figures are rotated to the same orientation, the Rectangles do not have the same fill as those in the other figures.

Chapter Eighteen
Codes
Exercise 18: 1

1) **e** - H - Square; Q - Black Fill.

2) **b** - T - Solid Outline; G - Rotation of Trapezium.

3) **d** - A - Solid Outline; Y - Pentagon.

4) **e** - C - Churn Shape points to the left; N - Large figure.

5) **c** - A - Parallelogram; V - Grey Fill.

6) **a** - S - Pentagon points up; K - Two shapes.

7) **b** - Y - Quadrant; O - Dashed Outline.

8) **d** - F - Horizontal figure; B - One linkage, one overlay.

9) **d** - K - One bone enclosed; N - Shield Shape.

10) **e** - B - Horizontal Line Fill; J - Small Circle enclosed.

11) **a** - N - Enclosed line figure; G - House Shape.

12) **a** - L - White Fill on the right; C - Circle on base.

13) **c** - W - Chevron Shape; A - Grey Fill.

14) **c** - P - Triangles have Grey Fill; M - Hexagon has Lattice Fill.

15) **b** - B - Medium figure; S - Black Fill.

16) **e** - Y - One shape; Q - Circle.

17) **c** - A - Pencil Shape points to the left; S - White Fill.

18) **a** - N - Enclosed Bone Shape is vertical; H - Speaker Shape.

19) **e** - Z - Star inner shape; J - Star outer shape.

20) **c** - V - Star points downwards; F - Thick Outline.

Exercise 18: 2

1) **b** - N - Dashed Outline; X - Flower Shape.

2) **a** - E - Vertical Line Fill; S - Two Circles have Black Fill.

3) **a** - T - Pentagon; G - Rotated Cross enclosed.

4) **c** - B - Dashed Outline; X - Medium enclosure.

5) **a** - H - Small figure; T - Chevron Shape points upwards.

6) **d** - N - Arrow points downwards; E - Star positioned in top left corner.

7) **c** - B - Cross Shape; X - Grey and White Fills.

8) **b** - L - Rotation of Quadrant; P - Quadrant positioned in bottom left corner.

9) **e** - L - Triangle and Square; P - Grey and White Fill.

10) **e** - L - Curved Arrow points left; Q - Diagonal Line Fill.

11) **c** - M - Grey Fill; X - Fill in top left quadrant.

12) **c** - Q - Helmet Shape; J - Enclosed H Shape.

13) **b** - G - Square; S - Enclosed shape has Dotted Outline.

14) **a** - B - Figure positioned diagonally; H - Heart Shape positioned at end of Cigar Shape.

15) **e** - J - Cross with White Fill enclosed in shape with Black Fill; Y - Both Squares have Grey Fill.

Answers

16) **a** - E - Both Crosses have White Fill;
P - Crosses are positioned vertically on the right.

17) **d** - G - Quadrant points upwards;
R - Bulb Shape points to the right.

18) **c** - M - Pentagon; I - Four shapes.

19) **b** - Y - Arrow positioned on the right;
F - Circle has single Solid outline.

20) **a** - Y - Grey Fill; L - Horizontal Line Fill.

Exercise 18: 3

1) **a** - X - Large Heart Shape points upwards;
C - Small Heart Shape on the right;
H - Small Heart Shape points upwards.

2) **d** - P - Circle; B - Solid Outline; V - Left Slant Line Fill.

3) **c** - K - Orientation of Bean Shape;
B - Horizontal Line Fill if Bean Shape is positioned vertically; T - Enclosed Circle has White Fill.

4) **b** - Y - Large Ellipse; E - Large Rectangle;
V - Grey Fill.

5) **e** - Q - Large figure; X - Thick Outline;
L - White Fill.

6) **d** - H - Two Lines; T - Stretched Cigar Shape; M - Vertical Lines.

7) **d** - D - Dotted Outline; P - Arrow points to the left; A - Medium Arrow.

8) **c** - R - Star; M - Four enclosed Circles;
P - White Fill.

9) **e** - A - Single Triangle points upwards;
Y - Single Triangle has White Fill;
L - One Grey Fill.

10) **a** - A - White Fill; L - Pencil Shape;
Z - Pencil Shape points upwards.

11) **e** - S - Square; Q - Black Fill; B - Four sections.

12) **c** - T - Black Circle enclosed; G - Helmet Shape points to the right; C - Cigar Shape enclosed.

13) **a** - Q - Rotated Cross; Y - Shield Shape;
C - House Shape.

14) **d** - B - Rotation of General Quadrilateral;
L - Grey Fill; F - Medium figure.

15) **b** - K - Enclosed shape has Grey Fill;
V - Large shape has Speckled Fill;
B - Enclosed Star is rotated.

16) **e** - O - Horizontal figure; C - Circles;
U - Four shapes.

17) **c** - F - Outer Circle has Black Fill;
Y - Inner Circle has Horizontal Line Fill;
P - Middle Circle has White Fill.

18) **a** - Z - Enclosed shape has Grey Fill;
I - Enclosed shape is positioned at bottom right or outer shape; M - Wide Line Fill.

19) **d** - A - Linkage has Black Fill; T - Figure is diagonal; O - Sectors.

20) **e** - R - Semi-circle has Dotted Outline;
W - Ellipse is enclosed; T - Ellipse has Solid Outline.

Exercise 18: 4

1) **e** - S - Arrow has Grey Fill; X - Black Outer Circle; B - Arrow points to the left;
L - Enclosed Circle has White Fill.

2) **b** - P - Dotted Outline; G - Two enclosed Circles; C - Sea Horse Shape is horizontal; V - Circles have White Fill.

3) **e** - M - Solid Outline; E - Enclosed Pentagon has White Fill; R - Large Pentagon points upwards; F - Large Pentagon has Lattice Fill.

4) **c** - T - Three Squares; X - Small Squares overlay large Square; A - Dashed Outline;
L - Enclosed Square with Black Fill.

5) **d** - A - Large shape has White Fill;
Y - Enclosed shape has Black Fill;
J - Enclosed shape is a Set Square Shape;
Q - Shield Shape.

6) **b** - M - Triangles; E - Point to point horizontally; U - Horizontal reflection;
B - Grey and White Fills.

7) **a** - L - Grey Fill; S - Three Crosses;
X - Vertical Cross; C - Pencil Shape points upwards.

8) **c** - P - Four lines and shapes; F - Grey Fill; D - Decreasing in height;
R - Squares.

9) **d** - D - Triangle points upwards;
M - Grey Fill; Z - Enclosed Circle;
G - Spike Shape points right.

10) **a** - D - Horizontal; X - Linkage has Black Fill; Q - Circles; J - Left Slant Lined Fill.

Answers

11) **e** - E - Black Fill; X - Dashed Outline;
M - Heart Shape on top right point of
Pentagon; B - Heart Shape points to the
right.

12) **e** - S - Enclosed Pentagon; X - Enclosed
shape has Lattice Fill; F - Circle;
B - Large shape has Grey Fill.

13) **c** - D - Spike Shape points upwards;
K - Enclosed shape has Black Fill;
Q - Enclosed Square; Y - No enclosed
line.

14) **b** - S - Large enclosed Triangle has Black
Fill; B - Small enclosed Triangle has
Black Fill; K - Triangle points to the left.
G - One enclosed line.

15) **c** - T - Vertical Figure; C - Black Fill;
Z - Circle; L - Two shapes.

16) **c** - P - Small Flower Shape; N - Dashed
Outline; B - Small shape enclosed in
bottom shape; G - Hexagons.

17) **e** - F - Thin Solid Outline; R - Enclosed
Cross Shape; Z - Two enclosed shapes;
V - Quadrant points upwards.

18) **a** - B - Circle has Horizontal Lined Fill;
L - Moon Shape at the top; Z - Moon
Shape has White Fill; P - Three Circles
have Grey Fill.

19) **c** - Z - Star Shape; G - Enclosed Phone
Shape; O - Enclosed shape has Black Fill;
U - Large shape has Grey Fill.

20) **b** - R - Enclosed Circles;
B - Parallelogram; Z - White Fill; J - Four
enclosed shapes.

Exercise 18: 5

1) **d** - U - Curved Arrow points to the left;
Q - Grey Fill.

2) **c** - T - Solid Outline; J - Same shapes.

3) **e** - N - Pentagons; C - Two shapes;
Y - White Fill.

4) **a** - X - Arrow points downwards;
G - Figure in bottom right of square.

5) **c** - N - White Fill; P - Thick outline;
F - Pentagon points to the left; Z - Large
figure.

6) **d** - G - Line ending has Black Fill;
M - Bulb Shape points downwards.

7) **d** - Z - Overlay; N - Loaf Shape;
Q - Square line ending; V - Line at the
top.

8) **b** - U - Squares have Black Fill;
Q - Speaker Shape has Grey Fill;
G - Speaker Shape points to the left.

9) **a** - B - Right-angled Triangle;
J - Horizontal Lined Fill.

10) **e** - G - Horizontal Lined Fill when Sector
points downwards; X - Tip has White Fill;
P - Sector points to the right.

11) **a** - B - Left Triangle has White Fill;
J - Right Triangle has Grey Fill; M - Left
Triangle points to the left; F - Right
Triangle points to the right.

12) **a** - D - Two shapes; L - Flower Shapes.

13) **d** - S - Wizard's Hat Shape has Grey Fill;
C - Small Circle has Black Fill;
K - Rotated Crosses; Q - Figure points
downwards.

14) **c** - W - Outer Shape is horizontal
6-pointed Star Shape; F - Enclosed Shape
is 5-pointed Start Shape.

15) **c** - B - Speaker Shape; R - Lattice Fill.

16) **b** - J - Three enclosed Lines; R - Small
shape is 6-pointed Star Shape;
Z - Shield Shape points upwards;
A - Small shape is under Shield Shape.

17) **c** - X - Three enclosed Moon Shapes;
F - Helmet Shape points downwards;
K - Moon Shapes point downwards.

18) **a** - B - White Fill; L - Four-sided outer
shape; S - Chevron Shape points to the
left.

19) **b** - C - Medium-sized figure; H - Black
Fill.

20) **b** - Q - Octagon has Left Slant Lined Fill;
X - Cross has Horizontal Lined Fill.

Chapter Nineteen

Analogies

Exercise 19: 1

1) **b** - The shape flips horizontally.

2) **e** - One side is added to the shape.

3) **a** - The fills swap.

4) **c** - The figure rotates 180°.

Answers

5) **e** - The Lined Fill rotates 90°.

6) **b** - The fills swap.

7) **d** - The figure flips horizontally.

8) **a** - The right half of the top enclosed shape and the bottom half of the bottom enclosed shape are subtracted.

9) **c** - The right half of the shape is subtracted.

10) **c** - The outer shapes are removed, leaving the middle shape and the linkages.

11) **b** - The ends of the lines are connected by Straight lines to become lines of symmetry.

12) **e** - The shapes swap.

13) **a** - The shape is split in half and separated out.

14) **d** - The figure flips horizontally.

15) **d** - The figure flips horizontally.

16) **b** - The shape increases in size.

17) **e** - A replica of the original shape is added as an overlay.

18) **a** - The line types swap.

19) **c** - The inner shape vertically transposes so the enclosed shape moves to above the large shape.

20) **a** - The shape becomes the linkage shape of two identical perpendicular shapes.

Exercise 19: 2

1) **e** - The top shape increases in size to become the outer shape. The bottom shape becomes the enclosure.

2) **a** - The figure flips horizontally. The fills swap.

3) **a** - The Grey Fill becomes White. A Square with a Black Fill is added as an overlay to each side.

4) **c** - The shape rotates 90° anticlockwise, then flips horizontally. The Solid Outline becomes Dashed.

5) **a** - The shape reduces in size and becomes the top shape. A duplicate of the smaller shape with a White Fill is added below.

6) **b** - The figure rotates 90°. The fill of the left shape becomes Grey.

7) **a** - One side is subtracted from each shape.

8) **d** - One side is subtracted from the shape. The Solid Outline becomes Dashed.

9) **b** - The shapes swap, with the fills staying in the same position. The Lined Fill rotates 90°.

10) **d** - The shape flips vertically. The Solid Outline becomes Dashed.

11) **e** - The shapes swap with their fills. A Square with a Thick Outline is added surrounding the figure.

12) **d** - The large shapes flip vertically and swap positions. The small shape remains in the same position in the top shape.

13) **a** - The shapes swap. The outline of the new inner shape becomes Solid.

14) **b** - The figure rotates 90° anticlockwise. The Black Fill becomes White.

15) **e** - The figure rotates 45° anticlockwise. The Solid Outline becomes Dotted.

16) **c** - The shapes swap with their fills. The Lined Fill rotates 90°.

17) **d** - One shape becomes an overlay. The outline of the bottom shape becomes Dashed.

18) **a** - The Grey Fill becomes White. A Dotted Outline is added.

19) **e** - The shapes rotate 180° individually.

20) **b** - The shape flips vertically. The smaller section becomes Grey.

Exercise 19: 3

1) **e** - The figure flips horizontally. The Solid Outline of the outer shape becomes Dotted. The Grey Fill becomes White.

2) **d** - The Black Fill becomes Grey. The shapes move up one line.

3) **b** - The shape reduces in size and becomes the bottom shape. A duplicate of the smaller shape is added as the top shape. The Lined Fill of the top shape is rotated 90°.

4) **a** - The inner shape rotates 90°. A replica of the inner shape is moved to each corner.

5) **e** - The figure rotates 90° clockwise. The Thick enclosed line becomes Thin Dashed. The Black Fill becomes Grey.

Answers

6) **b** - The shape reduces in size and is duplicated. The Cross-hatched Fill is split into the two opposite Lined Fills. The right shape is higher than the left shape.

7) **c** - The figure flips horizontally. The Black and White Fills swap.

8) **b** - A Liquid Fill is added to the shape. A duplicate of the original shape with a Dashed Outline is added to the left. The left shape rotates 180°.

9) **e** - The shapes swap. The Grey Fill becomes Black. The figure rotates 90° anticlockwise.

10) **b** - The enclosed line rotates 90° and becomes Dotted. The enclosed shapes stay in the same rotation and move clockwise to stay on either side of the line.

11) **e** - A duplicate of the large shape with a 90° rotation is added under the original shape. The enclosed shape horizontally transposes to outside the figure on the same side.

12) **c** - The figure rotates 90° clockwise. The Black Fill becomes White. The Solid Outline of the inner shape becomes Dotted. The enclosed shape rotates 180°.

13) **a** - The White Fill becomes Grey. Two sides are added to the shape. The Thin Outline becomes Thick.

14) **e** - The figure flips vertically. The Thin Outline of the bottom shape becomes Thick. The shapes swap fills.

15) **b** - The Solid Outline becomes Dashed. The Arrows flip and move around the Square.

16) **a** - The figure reduces in size and becomes the central enclosed shape. A replica of the original shape with a White Fill is added surrounding the enclosed shape. A larger replica shape with a Dashed Outline is added surrounding the new figure.

17) **c** - The White Fill becomes Mottled. A smaller replica shape with a 90° anticlockwise rotation is added as an overlay.

18) **d** - The shape is enlarged. A replica of the enlarged shape with a Grey Fill is added as an overlay. The original shape rotates 180°.

19) **b** - A replica shape with a 90° rotation and a Dashed Outline is added as a linkage.

20) **c** - The fill in the middle left square horizontally transposes. The fill in the bottom left square horizontally transposes. The Cross rotates 45°.

Exercise 19: 4

1) **b** - The shape rotates 90° anticlockwise. The shape is split into two and the new bottom shape is flipped. A White Fill is added to the new top shape.

2) **c** - The shape is enlarged and the fill becomes White. Small replica shapes with a Grey Fill are added as overlays to each corner.

3) **d** - The fill of the Square becomes Grey. A replica of the figure with a 180° rotation is added as an overlay and the outline becomes Dashed.

4) **a** - The shape is enlarged and rotates 180°. A replica of the enlarged shape with a Grey Fill is added as an overlay.

5) **a** - The figure rotates 180°. The enclosed shape reduces in size and the fill changes to Black. Replicas of the enclosed shape are put in each corner.

6) **d** - One side is added to each shape. The fills swap. The outline becomes Thick.

7) **c** - The figure rotates 90° anticlockwise. The line types swap.

8) **c** - The shape enlarges and rotates 180°. A duplicate shape with a half-Grey and half-White Fill is added behind this shape.

9) **e** - The line types swap. The Black Fills become White. The Grey Fill becomes Black.

10) **a** - The larger shape rotates 180°. The inner shape rotates 90° anticlockwise. The fills swap.

Answers

11) **c** - The figure rotates 45°. The Black Fill becomes White. The outline of the enclosed shape becomes Dashed.

12) **b** - The White and Black Fills swap. The figure rotates 90° anticlockwise. The short line vertically transposes. The Square line ending of the short line becomes a Circle.

13) **d** - The Grey Fill becomes White. The Black Fill becomes White. The Solid Outline becomes Dotted. The figure rotates 180°.

14) **b** - The fill of the inner shape becomes Black and the shape becomes the overlay on each corner of the outer shape. The original outer shape rotates 45° and the fill becomes Grey.

15) **a** - The other half of the large shape is added on so the large shape encloses the two smaller shapes. The figure rotates 180°. The fills of the smaller shapes swap.

16) **d** - The Solid Outline becomes Dashed. The enclosed shape rotates 180° and the fill becomes Black. The enclosed shape is duplicated and a Line is added in the middle of the large shape, separating the two enclosed shapes.

17) **c** - The figure rotates 180°. The Grey Fill becomes White. The fills of the outer and inner Squares swap. Dashed and Dotted lines are added to the left of the Solid line.

18) **e** - The shape vertically reflects. The White Fill becomes Black. A shape with the same number of sides as the number of points on the Star Shape is added surrounding the Star Shape. A Circle is added as an overlay on each corner.

19) **a** - The figure flips horizontally. The fills move one position inwards. The fill of the small shape becomes Black.

20) **b** - A larger replica of the shape with a 90° rotation is added. The Lined Fill rotates 90°. A replica shape with a Thick Outline is added around this figure. The original shape overlays the bottom of the figure.

Exercise 19: 5

1) **d** - The figure flips horizontally. The opposite Lined Fill is added to create a Cross-hatched Fill.

2) **b** - The figure reduces in size and rotates 180°. A duplicate of the smaller shape with a 180° rotation and a White Fill is added as an overlay.

3) **e** - The Solid Outline becomes Dashed. The enclosed shape rotates 180°. The left overlay rotates 180° and the fill becomes Grey. The fill of the right overlay becomes White.

4) **b** - The shape rotates 90° clockwise and reduces in size to become the top shape. A duplicate of this shape becomes the bottom shape. The original shape rotates 180° clockwise and reduces in size to become the middle shape. The fill of the middle shape becomes Grey.

5) **d** - The fills swap. The Lined Fill rotates 90°. The outline becomes Thick.

6) **d** - The Arrow rotates 180°. The shapes swap.

7) **b** - The outer linked shapes are removed.

8) **e** - The outline becomes Dashed.

9) **e** - The outline becomes Thick Solid. The Curved shape becomes Straight-edged.

10) **b** - The shape rotates 45° anticlockwise.

11) **c** - The shape rotates 180°. A replica shape with a Grey Fill is added as an enclosure. Smaller replicas of the shape with a Black Fill are added as enclosures at each corner.

12) **c** - One side is added to the shape. The shape reduces in size and a replica shape with a White Fill is added. The Lined Fill rotates 90°. The original shape overlays the shape with a White Fill.

13) **b** - The line types swap.

14) **d** - Half of the shape is removed.

15) **c** - The figure rotates 90° anticlockwise. A Black Fill is added to the left of the central shape.

16) **c** - The inner shape reduces in size and the fill becomes Grey. The shape then overlays each corner of the large shape. The fill of the large shape becomes White.

17) **a** - The figure rotates 180°. The outline becomes Thick. The fill of the new left shape becomes Black. The new right shape rotates 45°.

18) **e** - The inner shape rotates 90° anticlockwise. The fills swap.

19) **d** - The figure rotates 180°. The smallest shape changes fill. A Thick Outline that is the same colour as the fill is added around the shape. The fill of the shape becomes White. A small replica shape with a Dashed outline is added as the central enclosure.

20) **e** - The figure reflects horizontally. The Dashed Outline becomes Solid. The original shape with a Dashed Outline becomes an overlay.

<u>WHAT MALORY TOWERS SAID</u>

Jolly well done, Shreya! - Freddie

Miss Peters is happy! - Lucy and Julie

You've completed 4 books already!

Darrel is looking forward to you completing all of the books! - Felicity

Golly! You only have 4 workbooks left!

I'm sure that Alicia is really happy! - June

Congrats! - Susan

Great job! - Nora

Malory Towers is proud of you! - Pam

I'm so happy for you! - Bonnie

PROGRESS CHART

Exercise	Mark	%
17: 1		
17: 2		
17: 3		
17: 4		
17: 5		
18: 1		
18: 2		
18: 3		
18: 4		
18: 5		
19: 1		
19: 2		
19: 3		
19: 4		
19: 5		

**Overall
Percentage**

%

CERTIFICATE OF

ACHIEVEMENT

This certifies

Shreya Deshmukh - Y5

has successfully completed

11+ Non-verbal Reasoning
Year 5–7
WORKBOOK **4**

Overall percentage
score achieved

%

Comment _____

_____

Signed _____

(teacher/parent/guardian)

Date _____